Centaur Classics

General Editor : J. M. COHEN

FRANCISCO DE QUEVEDO

VISIONS

AS TRANSLATED BY SIR ROGER L'ESTRANGE
AND NOW INTRODUCED BY J. M. COHEN

SOUTHERN ILLINOIS
UNIVERSITY PRESS
CARBONDALE   ILLINOIS

© CENTAUR PRESS LTD. 1963

Published in the United States by
Southern Illinois University Press
Library of Congress Catalog No.
62 - 14998

Printed in Great Britain

CONTENTS

		PAGE
	INTRODUCTION BY J. M. COHEN	7
I	THE ALGUAZIL OR CATCHPOLE POSSESSED	15
II	OF DEATH AND HER EMPIRE	25
III	OF THE LAST JUDGMENT	49
IV	OF LOVING FOOLS	59
V	OF THE WORLD	69
VI	OF HELL	83
VII	OF HELL REFORMED	115

INTRODUCTION

Sᴵʀ Roger L'Estrange, one of the best prose stylists of the Restoration, led an adventurous and not altogether prosperous life as a political adventurer, Tory pamphleteer and professional writer. "A man of excellent parts", according to John Evelyn, "abating some affectations", though a consistent Royalist and Protestant he was never entirely trusted by his own side and much distrusted by the other. Receiving very little encouragement from Charles II, he gained a knighthood and nothing else from James II, with whose Catholicism he was out of sympathy, and was stripped of his office as "surveyor of the imprimery"—that is to say literary censor—on the accession of William and Mary. One of the first professional men-of-letters, he knew the hardships and humiliations of Grub Street life. For his voluminous works, never likely to be collected even by the most industrious editor, contain much polemical journalism that was deservedly forgotten almost as soon as written. He produced, however, a number of first-class translations, which continued to be read till well into the 18th century. His *Seneca's Morals by way of abstract* ran through ten editions; his version of the *Letters of a Portuguese Nun,* his Terence, his *Colloquies of Erasmus,* and his *Aesop's Fables,* all enjoyed a well-deserved popularity; and his *Visions of Quevedo,* here reprinted for the first time in fifty years, were reprinted no less than a dozen times within a century of their first appearance in 1667. One of the masterpieces of Spanish literature, it exists in no other English version. Indeed it would try a modern translator to the uttermost; and probably even then he would not improve on L'Estrange's free rendering, which is often closest to the spirit of Quevedo when it takes the greatest liberties with his actual words and sentences.

Roger L'Estrange was born at Hunstanton in 1616, and died in 1704, within a few days of his 88th birthday. In the Civil War, he fought in Prince Rupert's troop of cavalry, and was captured by the Parliamentarians while attempting to procure the surrender of Hunstanton, of which his father had been governor, and which he had lost to Cromwell's men in the early days of

7

the war. Roger L'Estrange's plot to obtain entrance into this stoutly Parliamen-
tary town was betrayed by "a brace of villains by name Lemon and Haggar",
and after facing a Court Martial, he was sentenced to death in 1644. In the
17th century, however, the judicial murder of political opponents was less
customary than today. Though L'Estrange lay for more than a year in "a
distressing condition of expectancy", the governor of Newgate obligingly contrived his escape, considering him "one in whom there was no more danger".
This quickly proved untrue, for no sooner was L'Estrange free than
he endeavoured to organise a Royalist rising in Kent. On its failure he fled to
Holland, but returned in 1653, trusting to an Act of Indemnity. On arriving in
London, he obtained a personal interview with Cromwell, and was released on
£2,000 security. He claimed to have bribed the Protector's attendants, but his
own party considered him compromised, and he seems to have forfeited their
confidence again. They accused him indeed of having further dealings with
Cromwell. He however denied this, saying that his only subsequent meeting
with the Protector had been at the house of some friends, where he had been
playing the bass-viol in a chamber-concert. The incident earned him the nickname of "Cromwell's fiddler", which stuck to him for a long time. He was in fact
a very competent and enthusiastic musician, as was noted by Samuel Pepys, and
a friend of the "Composer in ordinary" to Charles II, Matthew Locke.

In the last year of the Republic, L'Estrange entered polemical journalism.
After issuing a number of broadsides against Cromwell's possible successor,
General Lambert, he made a personal attack on the "Secretary in Foreign
Tongues to the Council of State", John Milton. A volley of pamphlets followed,
but L'Estrange had to wait three years for the first sign of encouragement from
the restored monarch. Then after conducting a vituperative attack on the freedom of the press, he was rewarded with the office of "surveyor of the imprimery".
This did not remove him from the field of polemical journalism, but enabled
him to publish his own, while suppressing the pamphlets of his opponents. He
was said to be remorseless in his persecution of all Whig printers, except those
that had pretty wives. An enthusiastic amorist, L'Estrange was unlucky in his
marriage, his wife being addicted to gambling. Such was his reputation for
lechery that his early nickname was no sooner forgotten than he earned himself
another, "The Dog Towzer".

L'Estrange's translations and his polemical journalism, supplementing his
salary as censor, earned him a modest living, which his wife squandered. Moreover, in 1677, he found himself in serious difficulties with his own party. Having

published evidence against the imposter Titus Oates, whose alleged Popish Plot enjoyed general credence, he fled once more to Holland, and was burned in effigy by the London mob. On his return he founded one of the first newspapers, *The Observator*. But the Earl of Arlington, a minister of the Crown, started *The Intelligencer* in competition, and this afterwards became *The London Gazette*. When forced to close down, L'Estrange claimed that *The Observator* had made him £400 a year, but that he had had to spend £500 "entertaining spies for information". Strangely enough, nevertheless, he was extremely angry with Arlington for relieving him of his losing enterprise.

James II gave Roger L'Estrange his knighthood, and a seat in Parliament for Winchester. He did not, however, reward him further. For, although in the past he had been accused of Catholicism, L'Estrange was throughout his life a strong and consistent anti-Catholic. He was also an opponent of Toleration. Consequently at the Glorious Revolution, he not only lost his "surveyorship", but was arrested in 1698. He was now eighty-two, and though his pen was still sharp he could do little harm to the new régime, which released him within a year. Six years later he died.

Sir Roger L'Estrange's experience as pamphleteer and journalist, the first according to Doctor Johnson "who regularly enlisted himself under the banner of a party for pay, and fought for it through right and wrong", greatly influenced his method of translation. Coming at the end of a long stream of amateurs, the great Elizabethan and Jacobean translators of whom Sir Thomas North, famous for his Plutarch, was one of the earliest and best, L'Estrange was a more professional craftsman. As in his journalism, he had always an audience in view, on whose approval and on whose purchase of his books he depended for a livelihood. His practice therefore was just the reverse of that of his fellow royalist Sir Thomas Urquhart, whose Rabelais was the last triumphant product of the Elizabethan and Jacobean school of translators. Urquhart's version of *Gargantua* and *Pantagruel*, published in 1653, and followed some thirty years after his death by his rendering of the *Third Book,* is a work of exuberant inaccuracy. While faithful to the spirit of the original, Urquhart made no attempt to translate the work in the style and manner of his own day. His Rabelais is even more verbose and digressive than the original. L'Estrange, on the other hand, faced with an original that provided almost as many syntactical complications and far-fetched allusions as *Gargantua,* already in 1667—the year in which *The Visions* appeared—anticipated the translator's technique advocated thirteen years later by John Dryden in the essay on translation with which he prefaced his version of Ovid's epistles. L'Estrange rendered the Spaniard Francisco de Quevedo, whose book was forty years old and belonged to a very different world from that of the Restoration, "in words such as he would probably have written if he were living and an Englishman". In this he differs greatly from Urquhart. His practice indeed is much closer to that of the Huguenot Peter Motteux, who completed Urquhart's Rabelais in a more work-aday spirit, and produced in his version of *Don Quixote* the most readable and the least scrupulous adaptation which that work had yet received.

Where Motteux was carelessly turning out translations for a living, and to suit a public which would not be too critical of his shortcomings, L'Estrange was scrupulously recasting a book which, rendered literally, would have puzzled and repelled the English readers of his day in a form in which they continued to enjoy it for more than a century. If there are resemblances between these *Visions* and *The Battle of the Books* or even *Gulliver's Travels*, it is because L'Estrange anticipated by almost half a century the deceptively simple prose style—so different from Quevedo's—of his fellow-pamphleteer, Jonathan Swift.

Let us take a passage from the fifth *Vision*, in which the narrator is being taken on a tour of the World—the world inside out (*El munda por de dentro*) is the original title of this vision—by a poor and tattered person "of a venerable age", who rejoices in showing him the deceptiveness of all appearances. The old man's speech on the villainy of lawyers is cut short by the entrance of another butt of Quevedo's angry wit, a fashionable courtier :

"My good old friend would have proceeded, if he had not been taken off by the rattling of a gilt coach, and a courtier in it, that was blown up as big as pride and vanity could make him. He sat stiff and upright, as if he had swallowed a stake, and made it his glory to show himself in that posture : it would have hurt his eyes to have exchanged a glance with any thing that was vulgar, and therefore he was not too profuse of his looks. He had a deep laced ruff on, that was right Spanish, which he wore erect, and so stiff starched, that a man would have thought he carried his head in a paper lanthorn. He was a great studier of set faces, and much affected with looking politic and big; but for his arms and body he had entirely lost or forgotten the use of them : he could neither bow nor move his hat to any man that saluted him; nor so much as turn from one side to the other, but sat as if he had been boxed up like a Bartholomew baby".

Though the style of the translation, and also the attitude of pessimistic scorn for mankind's pretentions that pervades Quevedo's writings, remind the reader that L'Estrange was a forerunner of Swift, the differences between *The Visions* and *Gulliver's Travels* are as many as the resemblances. Swift's gift of intellectual invention was most evident in the situations he contrived. His parody of voyages of travel, his satire at the expense of scientific theory, his play with relativity of size and position in the scale of being, all belong to a tradition of thought that goes back to Cyrano de Bergerac, to Rabelais, and to the *True History* of the Greek satirist Lucian. Quevedo, on the other hand, was treating the common-places of his time: the deceptions of court life, the scheming villainies of lawyers, the extortions of moneylenders, the wiles of pimps and whores, the fraudulent claims of physicians and apothecaries. It is with these contemporary figures that he peoples the hell of his *Visions*. His originality is one of language rather than of situation.

Consequently L'Estrange, confronted with a text in which word-play is more important than plain statement, was compelled to adopt a policy which no doubt would have appealed to him in any case. He did not translate literally but recast Quevedo's prose, passage by passage. One looks in vain for anything in the Spanish that could have prompted the alliterative felicity of the last words of the quotation. Nothing that Quevedo wrote justifies the comparison of this ridiculous courtier in his coach to a doll packed in a box and offered for sale at Bartholomew fair. Quevedo, on the other hand, invents some far-fetched comparisons that L'Estrange does not even attempt to get into English. Quevedo's courtier is so puffed-up that he appears to be trying to wrench his coach off its axles. His swelled chest is thus made to suggest some unnatural effort. L'Estrange contrives a similar effect more simply by means of the semi-proverbial notion that he must have swallowed a stake: a rendering at least half-justified by Quevedo's observation a few lines later that the man was as erect as if he wanted to boast of having been skewered (Iba tan derecho, preciándose de espetado). Then by means of a false antithesis common in the style of his day, the Spanish author says of his courtier that he is "sparing of his eyes and niggardly with his glances": a proposition which L'Estrange expands and naturalises to the extent of making the second statement follow on the first (it would have hurt his eyes . . . profuse of his looks).

As has been suggested, L'Estrange's method is to take Quevedo's conceits and recast them in the form of simple comparisons that will be palatable to an Englishman of his day. As a result, we are not conscious of reading a translation. The verbal tricks and flourishes of the original are removed and in exchange we are given picturesque turns of English, like the comparison to the Bartholomew baby or to the courtier's having seemed "to carry his head in a paper lanthorn".

A literal translation of Quevedo's book would even today, when we are more accustomed than the men of the Restoration to artificial styles, seem contrived and over-literary. Charles Duff, in his selection from Quevedo's work in various translations published in the *Broadway Translations* forty years ago, attempted to revise L'Estrange and bring him closer to his original. In fact, however, he merely added some passages that were missing from the present version, and altered some others in which he felt that L'Estrange's rendering was unnecessarily free. In doing so, however, he destroyed the stylistic unity of the original, to which we have gone back for this reprint. For L'Estrange's *Visions,* as Mr. Duff states in the introduction to his selection "is not only *the best we possess* but contains page after page of lively writing . . . There is no insipidity in it."

*　　*　　*　　*

There was no insipidity in anything that Francisco de Quevedo wrote. Born in Madrid in 1580, he was brought up at the gloomy court of Philip II, where his mother was a lady in waiting. His father died soon after his birth. Lame and appallingly short-sighted, he was crammed with learning, first by governesses and tutors, then at the Jesuit college of Madrid and finally at the University of Alcalá de Henares. Prodigiously over-educated in theology and philosophy, Latin, Greek and Hebrew, and later in Italian, French and Arabic, he plunged wildly into fashionable life, kept a mistress, fought duels and began to pour out a stream of savage and satirical verses which only ceased with his death. He quickly despaired of himself and his country. His pessimism was dark and unrelenting. Much of his best writing, including his picaresque novel *La vida del Buscón* (Life of a Petty Thief) and the present *Sueños* or Visions, in which he takes his reader for a tour of Hell and the Last Judgement, was finished when he was still in his twenties. Much of his poetry too, including his fantastic addresses to a variety of mistresses who do not seem to have granted him their favours, dates from this time.

Quevedo's satire is cruel and wholesale. He possessed no gift of analysis, but mercilessly attacked every class of person that he hated—judges, apothecaries, doctors, bankers, etc.—without the least discrimination. Something had gone wrong with his own life, and Spain was in decline. Therefore he threshed about him, striking angry blows at all those who might have been responsible. What saved him was his gift of fantasy. His hatred quickly dissolved in exuberant invention. The notion of a guided tour of hell was as old as the *Odyssey* or the sixth book of the Aeneid. Pictorially, hell had been portrayed in the heretical

15th century by Hieronymous Bosch, and was to be portrayed in the 18th by Quevedo's great admirer, Francisco de Goya in his last witch-haunted visions. But the *Sueños* present a hell of their own age, which reflects the low-life of the Capital, into which the ungainly and exasperated poet had thrown himself in an endeavour to escape from his deformities and his evil and introverted imagination. In the original, it is almost as exuberant as Rabelais. In L'Estrange's version, it is equally mordant and haunting, though in style a great deal more straightforward. The background, moreover, is subtly transferred from the Madrid of the early 17th century to Restoration London.

After his first period of literary production, Quevedo retired from Court, at the age of 32, and devoted himself to the study of theology and his favourite Stoic philosophy. But next year he was offered a post as political agent by the ambitious and cultured viceroy of Sicily, the Duque de Osuna. Quevedo served him for seven years, and acquired a first-hand experience of politics, which not only disillusioned him further, but wrecked his career. He was discovered while leading a plot to undermine the independence of Venice, and escaped from the city in disguise. Quarrelling with Osuna, he then returned to Spain, where he found himself in disgrace. At this point his master King Philip III died, Osuna fell from power, and Quevedo attached himself to the new favourite, the Conde Duque de Olivares, to whom he addressed one of his most famous poems, the *Epístola satírica y censoria*, which is in effect a plea to the new minister to restore the good old times of Spain's greatness. When these times were he does not make altogether explicit. Quevedo longs for the simplicity of the Roman republic, but also finds virtue in the heroic days of the reconquest of Spain from the Moors, and in the heroic empire-building age of Charles V. All that is wrong however lies in the present. In the best of his later sonnets, which are his supreme poetic achievement, Quevedo reverts to a vision of his country's decay. The decay was a fact; the reasons that Quevedo adduced for it were almost all false. Politically, he was naïve to the last.

For the next ten years Quevedo took no employment, but involved himself in countless suits and controversies. He could not live without someone or something to hate. His stoicism was an ideal which he could not practise. At the end of this time, when already 52, he was persuaded to marry. He had never been fortunate in love. Indeed, on the evidence of his poetry, one would not suppose that he had ever really been in love. So many angry attacks on women, fair, ugly, old, young, proud or accommodating, did not augur well for this late marriage, which lasted only a few months. The pair then separated.

Meanwhile the Count Duke's ministry had deteriorated into a dictatorship, and Quevedo seems to have joined some plot against the régime. Possibly he involved himself with French agents, possibly he did no more than protest in scurrilous verses which offended the king. In 1639 he was arrested and imprisoned in a monastery, from which he was released six months after the fall of Olivares. Weakened by three-and-a-half years of close confinement, he survived only two years more.

Quevedo's poetry has been compared to that of John Donne and his prose, already in this introduction, to Swift's. He must be valued, however, for his own qualities, which nowhere emerge more clearly than in the *Sueños*. His work is uneven, and much both of his poetry and his prose is hasty and imperfect. But these *Visions*, and particularly the second, *Of Death and her Empire*, originally called by Quevedo the *Visit in Jest* (Visita de los chistes), are not only his finest prose work, but are, as has been said, among the masterpieces of 17th century Spanish literature. In L'Estrange's translation they are also one of the few masterpieces of Restoration prose.

J.M.C.

London,
1962

I

THE ALGUAZIL
OR CATCHPOLE POSSESSED

As I was going a few days since to a convent in this city to hear mass, I saw a prodigious multitude of people endeavouring to get in, but I was told the gate was locked. A gentleman informed me, upon enquiring the reason of it, that a demoniac was to be exorcised: This made me as curious as the rest; but I was not more successful than they were, and therefore resolved to go home again. As I went along, an acquaintance met me, who belonged to the same convent; and he, perceiving my curiosity, having been told the same news that I had, bade me go with him, and he would gain me admittance: Accordingly, going to a little back-door, by showing a ticket he had, we both obtained entrance into the church, and from thence into the vestry. The first thing we beheld was a terrible looking fellow, all in rags, with a tippet about his neck, his hands tied behind his back, and roaring like a bull. Heaven preserve us, cried I, at the same time crossing myself, what is the matter with the man? Why, answered the reverend Father who was to perform the operation, he is possessed with a devil. That is an execrable falsehood, exclaimed the spirit that troubled him; it is not a man possessed with a devil, but a devil possessed with a man; therefore you ought to be more careful of what you say; for it is very obvious, both by the question and answer, that you are a parcel of idiots: For to tell you the truth, we devils never enter into the body of a Catchpole but by compulsion and therefore you should not say a Catchpole be-deviled, but a Devil be-catchpoled: And to give you your due, you men can deal better with us devils than with the catchpoles; for they make use of the cross to cover their villainy, whereas we do all in our power to avoid it.

15

If we are so different in our humours, yet we act pretty much alike in our offices; if we draw men into judgment and condemnation, so do catchpoles; we are desirous of the world's becoming more and more wicked, so are they; nay, and much more so than us, for they maintain their families by it, whereas we do it only for the sake of company. And in this catchpoles are worse than devils; they prey upon their own species, and worry one another, which we never do. For our parts, we are angels still, though black ones; and were turned into devils only for aspiring at an equality with our Creator : Whereas, the corruption of mankind is the generation of a catchpole. So that, my good Father, your labour is to no purpose in plying this wretch with reliques; for you may as soon redeem a soul from hell, as a prey out of his hands.

It very much astonished me to find the devil so great a sophister; but, notwithstanding all this, the holy man went on with his exorcism; and to stop the spirit's mouth, washed his face with holy water ; this made the demoniac ten times madder than before, and set him a roaring so horridly, that it deafened the company, and made the very walls shake. And now, says he, you may, perchance, imagine this extravagance to be the effect of your holy water; but let me tell you, that mere water would have done the same thing; for your catchpoles hate nothing in the world like water; especially that of a King's Bench pump.

Come, come, says the Father, there is no ear nor credit to be given to this rascal; set but his tongue at liberty, and you shall have him fall foul upon the government, and the ministers of justice, for keeping the world in order, and suppressing wickedness, because it spoils his market. No more chopping of logic, good Mr. Conjurer, says the devil, for there is more in it than you are aware of; if you will do a poor devil a good office, give me my despatch out of this wretched Alguazil; for I am a devil, you must know, of no small note, and shall never be able to endure the jests and affronts that will be put upon me at my return, for having kept this rascal company. All in good time, replied the Father, thou shalt have thy discharge; that is to say, in pity to this unhappy wretch, and not for thy own sake. But tell me first, what makes thee torment him thus? Nothing in the world, answered the devil, but a contest betwixt him and me, which was the greater devil of the two.

The reverend Father did not at all relish these wild and malicious replies; but to me the dialogue was very pleasant, especially being, by this time, a little familiarized with the demon. My good Father, said I, here are none but friends, and I may speak to you as my confessor, and the confident of all the secrets of my soul ; I am very desirous, with your leave, to ask the devil a few questions; and who knows, but a man may be the better for his answers, though, very probably, contrary to his intention? Keep him only, in the meantime, from tormenting this poor creature. The exorcist granted my request, and the spirit went on. Well, says he, smiling, the devil shall never want a friend at court, so long as there is a poet within the walls. And, indeed, the poets do us many a good turn, both by pimping and otherwise; but if you, said he, should not be kind to us, looking upon me, you will be thought very ungrateful, considering the honour of your entertainment now in hell. I asked him then, what store of poets they had? Prodigious numbers, says the devil; so many that we have been forced to make more room for them; nor is there anything in nature so pleasant as a poet in the first year of his probation; he comes laden with letters of recommendation to our superiors, and enquires very gravely for Charon, Cerberus, Rhadamanthus, Eacus, and Minos.

Well, said I, but in what manner are they punished? for I began now to make the poet's case my own. Their punishments, replied the devil, are many, and suited to the trade they drive. Some are condemned to hear other men's works; and this is the plague of the fiddlers too. We have others that are in for a thousand years, and yet still poring upon some old stanza they have made on their mistress. Some again are beating their foreheads with the palms of their hands, and even boring their very noses with hot irons, in rage that they cannot come to a resolution, whether they shall say face or visage; whether they shall say jail or gaol; whether cony or cunny, because it comes from *cuniculus,* a rabbit. Others are biting their nails to the quick, and at their wits end for a rhyme for chimney; and dozing up and down in a brown study, till they drop into some hole at last, and give us trouble enough to get them out again. But they that suffer the most, and fare the worst, are your comic poets, for whoring so many queens and princesses upon the stage, and coupling ladies of honour with footmen, and noblemen with common jilts, in the winding up of their plays; and for giving the bastinado to Alexander and Julius Caesar in their interludes and farces. Now, I must tell you, that we do not lodge these with other poets, but with petty-foggers and attorneys, as common dealers in the mystery of shifting, shuffling, forging, and cheating. And now for the discipline of hell: you must know we have incomparable harbingers and quarter-masters; insomuch, that let them come in whole caravans, as it happened the other day, every man is in his quarter in a moment.

There came to us a great many tradesmen; the first of them a poor rogue,

B

that made profession of drawing the long-bow; and him we were about to put among the armourers, but one of the company moved and carried it, that since he was so good at draughts, he might be sent to the clerks and scriveners; a sort of people that will fit you with draughts good and bad, of all sorts and sizes, and to all purposes. Another called himself a cutter: we asked him whether in wood or stone? Neither, said he, but in cloth and stuff, commonly called a tailor; and him we turned over to those that were in for detraction and calumny, and for cutting large thongs out of other men's leather. There was a blind fellow who would fain have been among the poets, but for likeliness sake we quartered him among the lovers. After him came a sexton, or, as he styled himself, a burier of the dead; and then a cook that was troubled in conscience for putting off cats for hares: these were despatched away to the pastry-men. We disposed of about half-a-dozen crack-brained fools among the astrologers and alchemists. In the number, there was one notorious murderer, and him we packed away to the gentlemen of the faculty, the physicians. The broken merchants we kennelled with Judas, for making ill bargains. Corrupt ministers and magistrates, with the thief on the left hand. The embroilers of affairs, and the tale-bearers, take up with the vintners; and the brokers with the Jews. In short, the policy of hell is admirable, where every man has his place suitable to his rank.

As I remember, said I, you were just now speaking of lovers; pray tell me, have ye many of them in your dominions? I ask, because I am myself a little subject to the itch of love, as well as poetry. Love, says the devil, is like a great spot of oil, that diffuses itself everywhere, and consequently hell cannot be sufficiently stocked with that sort of vermin. But let me tell you, we have many kinds of lovers; some dote upon themselves; others upon their pelf; these upon their own discourses; those upon their own actions; and once in an age, perchance, comes a fellow that dotes upon his own wife; but this is a great rarity, for the jades commonly bring their husbands to repentance, and then the devil may throw his cap at them. But, above all, for sport, if there can be any in hell, commend me to those gawdy coxcombs, who, by the variety of colours and ribbons they wear, favours, as they call them, one would swear they were only dressed up for a sample, or kind of inventory of all the gewgaws that are to be had at the mercers. Others you shall have so overcharged with peruque, that you will not easily know the head of a cavalier from the ordinary block of a tire-woman: And some again you would take for carriers, by their packets and bundles of love-letters; which being made combustible by the fire and flame they treat of, we are so thrifty of, as to employ upon singeing their own tails, for the saving of better fuel. But, oh! the pleasant postures of the maiden lover, when he is upon the practice of the gentle leer, and embracing the air for his mistress! Others we have that are condemned for feeling, and yet never come to the touch: These pass for a kind of buffoon pretenders; ever at the eve, but never at the festival. Some again have ruined themselves, like Judas, for a kiss.

One storey lower is the abode of contented cuckolds; a poisonous place, and strewed all over with the horns of rams and bulls. These are so well read in women, and know their destiny so well beforehand, that they never so much as trouble their heads for the matter. Ye come next to the admirers of old women; and these are wretches of so depraved an appetite, that if they were not kept tied up, and in chains, the very devils themselves could not resist them. The truth is, whatever you may think of a devil, he is regarded by them as a very Adonis.

Thus far I have satisfied your curiosity; a word now for your instruction. If you would make an interest in hell, you must give over that roguish way you have got of abusing the devils in your shows, pictures, and emblems: at one time, for instance, we are painted with claws or talons, like eagles or griffins; at another, we are dressed up with tails, like so many hackney-jades, with their fly-flaps; and now and then ye shall see a devil with a coxcomb. Now I will not deny, but some of us may, indeed, be very well taken for hermits and philosophers. If you can help us in this point, do; and we shall be ready to do you one good turn for another. I was asking Michael Angelo here a while ago, why he drew the devils in his great piece of the Last Judgment, with so many monkey-faces, and Merry-Andrew postures. His answer was, that he followed his fancy, without any malice in the world, for as then, he had never seen any devils; nor, indeed, did he believe that there were any; but he hath now learned the contrary to his cost. There is another thing, too, we take extremely ill; which is, that, in your ordinary discourses, you are out with your purse presently to every rascal, and call him devil. As for example: do you see how this devil of a tailor has spoiled my clothes? How that devil has made me wait? How that devil has cheated me? &c. All this is very ill done, and no small disparagement to our quality, to be ranked with tailors: a company of slaves, that serve us in hell only for brush-wood; and are obliged to beg hard to be admitted on any condition: though I confess they have possession on their sides, and custom, which is another law; being in possession of theft, and stolen goods, they make much more conscience of keeping your stuffs than your holidays, grumbling and domineering at every turn, if they have not the same respect with the children of the family. Ye have another trick, too, of giving everything to the devil that displeases you, which we cannot but take very unkindly. The devil take thee, says one; an excellent present, I warrant ye; but the devil has somewhat else to do, than to take and carry away all that is given him; if they will come of themselves, let them come, and welcome. Another gives that rascal of a valet to the devil; but the devil will have none of your valets, he thanks you for your love; a pack of rogues, that are for the most part worse than devils; and, to say the truth, they are good neither roast nor sodden. I give that Italian to the devil, cries a third: thank you for nothing: for ye shall have an Italian will trick the devil himself, and take him by the nose, like mustard. Some again will be for giving a Spaniard to the devil; but he has been so cruel wherever he has got footing, that we had rather have his room than his company, and make a present to the Grand Signior of his nutmegs.

Here the devil paused; and in the same instant, there happening a slight scuffle betwixt a couple of conceited coxcombs, which should go foremost, I turned to see the matter, and cast my eye upon a certain tax-gatherer that had ruined a friend of mine; and, in some sort, to revenge myself of this ass in a lion's skin, I asked the devil, whether they had not that sort of blood-suckers among the rest, in their dominions; an informing, projecting generation of men, and the very bane of a kingdom? You know little, says he, if you do not know these vermin to be the right heirs of perdition; and that they claim hell for their inheritance; and yet we are now even upon the point of discarding them; for they are so pragmatical, and ungrateful, that there is no bearing them. They are at this present time in consultation about an impost upon the highway to hell and, indeed, payments run so high already, and are so likely to increase too, that it is much feared in the end, we shall quite lose our trading and commerce. But if ever they come to put this in execution, we shall be so bold as to treat them next bout, by keeping them on the wrong side of the door, which will be worse than hell to them; for it leaves them no retreat, being expelled Paradise and Purgatory already. This race of vipers, said I, will never be quiet, till they tax the way to Heaven itself. Oh, replied the devil, that had been done long since, if they had found it worth their trouble; but they have had a factor abroad these ten years, that is glad to wipe his nose on his sleeve, still for want of a handkerchief. But pray upon what do they design to levy these new impositions? For that, answered the devil, there is a gentleman of the trade at your elbow can tell you all; pointing to my old friend the publican. This drew the eyes of the whole company upon him, and put him so out of countenance, that he plucked down his hat over his face, clapped his tail between his legs, and went his way, with which we were all of us well enough pleased; and then the devil continued. Well, said he, laughing, my voucher is departed, you see; but I think I can say as much to this point, as himself. The impositions now to be set on foot, are upon bare-necked ladies, patches, moleskins, Spanish paper and all the unnecessary part of the effeminate world; upon your capes a-la-mode, excess in apparel, collations, rich furniture, your cheating and blasphemy, your gaming ordinaries, and, in general upon whatsoever serves to advance our empire: so that, without a friend at court, or some good magistrate to help us out at a dead list, and stick to us, we may even shut up our shop, for you will find hell a very desert. Well, said I, methinks I see nothing in all this but what is very reasonable; for to what purpose serves it, but to corrupt good manners, stir up ill appetites, provoke and encourage all sorts of debauchery, destroy all that is good and honourable in human society, and chalk out, in effect, the ready way to the devil!

I heard you mention something just now of magistrates; I hope there are no judges in hell? You may as well imagine, cried the spirit, that there are no devils there; let me tell you, friend of mine, your corrupt judges are the great spawners that supply our lake; for what are those millions of catchpoles, proctors, attorneys, clerks, and barristers, that come sailing to us every day in shoals, but the fry of such judges? Nay, sometimes in a lucky year, for cheating, forging and forswearing, we can hardly find room to put them in.

Do you mean to infer from hence now, said I, that there is no justice upon earth? Very right, quoth the devil, for Astræa, which is the same thing, is fled, long since, to Heaven. Do you not know the story? Indeed, replied I, I do not. Then, quoth the devil, I will tell it you.

"It once happened, that Truth and Justice came together to take up their quarters upon earth; but the one being naked, and the other very severe and plain-dealing, they could not meet with any body that would receive them. At last, when they had wandered a long time, like vagabonds, in the open air, Truth was glad to take up her lodging with a mute; and Justice, perceiving that though her name was much used as a cloak to knavery, yet that she herself was in no esteem, took up a resolution of returning to Heaven. Before she departed, she bid adieu, in the first place to all courts, palaces and great cities, and went into the country, where she met with some few poor simple cottagers; but Malice and Persecution at last discovered her, and she was banished thence too. She next presented herself in many places, and people asked her what she was; she answered them, Justice; for she would not lie for the world. Justice! cried they, we know nothing of her: tell her, here is nothing for her, and shut the door. Upon these repulses she took wing and away she went to Heaven, hardly leaving so much as the bare print of her footsteps behind. Her name, however, is not yet forgotten; and she is pictured with a sceptre in her hand, and still called Justice". But give her what name you please, she makes as good a figure in hell as a tailor; and, for sleight of hand, puts down all the jilts, cheats, pick-locks, and trepanners in the world: to say the truth, avarice is grown to that height, that men employ all the faculties of soul and body to rob and deceive. The lecher, does he not steal away the honour of his mistress, though with her consent. The attorney picks your pocket, and shows you a law for it. The comedian gets your money and your time, by reciting other men's labours: the lover cozens you with his eyes; the eloquent man, with his tongue; the valiant with his arms; the musician with his voice and fingers; the astrologer with his calculations; the apothecary with sickness and health; the surgeon with blood; and the physician with death itself. In some sort or other they are all cheats; but the catchpole, in the name of Justice, abuses you with his whole man; he watches you with his eyes, follows you with his feet, seizes with his hands, accuses with his tongue, and, in fine, put it in your Litany. From catchpoles, as well as devils, good Lord, deliver us.

What is the reason, cried I, that you have not coupled women with the thieves; for they are both of a trade? Not a word of women, as you love me, replied the devil; for we are so tired out with their importunities, so deafened with the eternal clack of their tongues, that we start at the very thought of them: And to speak sincerely, hell were no ill winter quarters, if it were not so over-stocked with that sort of cattle. Since the death of the witch of Endor, it has been all their business to improve themselves in subtlety and malice, and to set us together by the ears among ourselves. Nay, some of them are so bold as to tell us, that when we have done our worst, they give us a Rowland for our Oliver. Only this comfort we have, that they are a cheaper plague to us than they are to you; for we have no public walks, concerts, or play-houses, in our territories, where they can go astray.

However, I perceive you are not ill stored with women, but of which have you most, said I, handsome or ill-favoured? Oh, of the ill-favoured, six to one, answered the devil; for your beauties can never want gallants to lay their appetites; and many of them, when they come at last to have their bellies full, even give over the sport, repent, and escape. Whereas nobody will touch the ill-favoured, without a pair of tongs; and, for want of water to quench their fire, they come to us such skeletons, that they are enough to terrify the devil himself: For they are most commonly old, and accompany their last groans with a curse upon the younger that are to survive them. I carried away one the other day of threescore and ten that I took just in the nick, as she was upon a certain exercise to remove obstructions: And when I came to land her, alas! the poor woman! what a terrible fit had she got of the tooth-ache! when, upon search, the devil a tooth had she left in her head; only she belied her chops, to save her credit.

I am very well satisfied, said I, in all your answers; but pray, once again, what store of beggars have you in hell? Poor people, I mean. Poor, cried the devil, who are they? Those, said I, that have no possessions in the world. How can that be, quoth he, that those should be damned, that have nothing in the world, when men are only damned for what they possess? To tell you the truth, I find none of their names in our books, which is no wonder: For he that has nothing to trust to, shall be left by the devil himself, in time of need. To deal plainly with you, where have you greater devils than your flatterers, false friends, good company and envious persons? than a son, a brother, or a relation, that lies in wait for your life, to get your fortune; that mourns over you in your sickness, and already wishes that the devil had you? Now the poor have nothing of this; they are neither flattered nor envied; nor befriended, nor accompanied: There is no gaping for their possessions; and, in short, they are a sort of people that live well, and die better; and there are some of them that would not exchange their rags for royalty itself: They are at liberty to go and come when they please, be it war or peace; free from cares, taxes, and public duties. They fear no judgments or executions, but live as inviolable, as if their persons were sacred. They take no thought for to-morrow; but setting a just value on their hours, they are good husbands of the present, considering that what is past, is as good as dead, and what is to come uncertain. But they say, When the devil preaches, the world is near an end.

The divine hand is in this, cried the reverend Father that performed the exorcism, thou art the Father of lies, and yet deliverest truths, able to mollify and convert a heart of stone. Do not you mistake yourself, said the devil, to suppose that your conversion is my business? I speak these truths to aggravate your guilt, and that you may not plead ignorance another day, when you shall be called to answer for your transgressions. It is true, most of you shed tears at parting; but it is the apprehension of death, and not true repentance, that works upon you; for you are all a pack of hypocrites; or, if at any time you entertain those reflections, your trouble is, that your body will not be able to answer your appetites and then you pretend to pick a quarrel with the sin that forsakes you.

Thou art an imposter, replied the exorcist, for there are many righteous souls that draw their sorrow from another fountain. But I perceive you have a mind to amuse us, and make us lose time, and, perchance, your own hour is not yet come, to quit the body of this miserable creature; however, I conjure thee, in the name of the Most High, to leave tormenting him, and to hold thy peace. The devil obeyed; and the good Father, turning to us, My friends, says he, though I verily believe that it is the devil who has talked to us all the while, through the organs of this miserable wretch, yet, he that sincerely considers what has been said, may profit by the discourse. Wherefore, without considering whence it came, remember that Saul, although a wicked prince, prophesied; and that honey has been extracted from the mouth of a lion. Withdraw then, and I shall make it my prayer, as it is my hope, that this terrifying and wonderful spectacle may lead you to a true sight of your errors, and, at last, make you forsake them, and turn to the paths of righteousness and equity.

II

OF DEATH AND HER EMPIRE

I HAVE made it a common remark, that mean souls generally breed sad thoughts, and in solitude, they gather in troops to assault the wretched, which is the trial wherein the coward does most betray himself; and yet I cannot, notwithstanding my utmost efforts, when I am alone, avoid those accidents and surprises in myself, which I condemn in others. I have sometimes, upon reading the grave and severe Lucretius, been seized with a surprising damp; whether from his striking counsels upon my passions, or some tacit reflection of shame upon myself, I know not. However, to render this confession of my weakness the more excusable, I will begin my discourse with somewhat out of that elegant and inimitable poet.

"Let us imagine", says he, "that a voice from Heaven should thus speak to any of us: What ails thee, O mortal man! or to what purpose is it to spend thy life in groans and complaints, under the fear of death! Where are thy past years and pleasures? Are they not vanished and lost in the flux of time, as if thou hadst put water into a sieve? Bethink thyself then of a retreat, and leave the world with the same content and satisfaction, as thou wouldst do a table genteelly furnished, and a merry company, upon a full stomach. Wretched mortal that thou art! thus to weary and torment thyself, when thou mayest live peaceably and with content".

This passage brought into my mind the words of Job, chap. xiv.; and I was carried on from one meditation to another, till at length I fell fast asleep over my book; which I ascribed rather to a favourable providence, than to my natural disposition. So soon as my soul felt herself at liberty, she entertained me with the following comedy, my fancy supplying both the stage and the actors.

25

In the first scene entered a troop of physicians, upon their mules, with deep housings, marching not very regularly, sometimes fast, sometimes slow, and, to say the truth, most commonly in a group. They were all wrinkled and withered about the eyes, I suppose with casting so many sour looks upon the urinals and close-stools of their patients; bearded like goats; and their faces so overgrown with hair, that their fingers could hardly find the way to their mouths : in the left hand they held the reins, and their glove, rolled up together; and in the right a cane, which they carried rather for show than correction; for they understood no other way of managing their animals but by the heels; and all along head and body went together, like a baker upon his panniers. Several of them, I observed, had huge gold rings upon their fingers, set with stones of so large a size, that they could hardly feel a patient's pulse, without minding him of his monument. There were a great many of them, with several puny licentiates at their heels, that came out graduates, by conversing rather with the mules than with the doctors. Well, said I to myself, if there requires no more than this to make a physician, it is no wonder we pay so dear for their experience.

These were followed by a vast multitude of apothecaries, laden with pestles and mortars, suppositories, spatulas, glister-pipes, and syringes, all ready charged, and as mortal as gun-shot; together with several boxes, intituled, "Remedies without, but poisons within". You may observe, that when a patient comes to die, the apothecary's mortar rings the passing bell, as the priest's requiem finishes the business. An apothecary's shop is, in effect, no other than the physician's armoury, that supplies him with weapons; and, to say the truth, the instruments of the apothecary and the soldier are much of a quality; what are their boxes, but pikes; their syringes, but pistols; and their pills, but bullets? Yet, after all, considering their purgative medicines, we may properly enough call their shops Purgatory; and why not their persons, Hell; their patients, the Damned; and their masters, the Devils? These apothecaries were in jackets, wrought all over with recipes, struck through like wounded hearts, and in the form of the first character of their prescription; which, as they tell us, signifies, "recipe, take thou"; but we find it to stand for "recipio, I take" : Next to this figure, they write, "ana"; which is as much as to say, "an ass, an ass"; and, last of all, the ounces and the scruples; an incomparable cordial to a dying man; the former to despatch the body, and the latter to put the soul into the highway to the devil. To hear them call over all their simples would make you swear they were raising so many devils; such as, Opopanex, Buphtalmas, Astaphylions, Alectorolophos, Ophioscorodon, Anemosphorus, and a great many more.

And by all this formidable bombast, is meant nothing in the world but a few simple roots, as carrots, turnips, skirrets, radishes, and the like. But they keep the proverb in remembrance, "He that knows thee will never buy thee"; and, therefore, everything must be made a mystery, to hold their patients in ignorance, and keep up the price of the market. And were not the very names of their medicines sufficient to fright away any distemper, it is to be feared the remedy would prove worse than the disease. Can any pain in nature, think you, have the confidence to look the physician in the face, that comes armed with a drug made of man's grease, though disguised under the name of mummy, to take off the horror and disgust of it? or, to stay for a dressing with Dr. Whacum's plaster, that shall fetch up a man's leg to the size of a mill-post? When I saw these people herded with physicians, I thought the old sluttish proverb that says, "There is a great distance between the pulse and the a—e", was wrong, for making such a difference in their dignities, for I find none at all; for the physician skips, in a trice, from the pulse to the stool and urinal, according to the doctrine of Galen, who sends all his disciples to those unsavoury oracles; from whose hands the devil himself, if he were sick, would not receive so much as a glister. Oh! these cursed and lawless arbitrators and disposers of lives! that, without either conscience or religion, divide our souls and bodies, by their damned poisonous potions, scarrifications, incisions, excessive bleedings, &s., which are but the several ways of executing their tyranny and injustice upon us.

After these came the surgeons, laden with pincers, crane-bills, catheters, disquamatories, dilators, scissors, and saws; and with them so dreadful an outcry of cut, tear, open, saw, flay, burn, that my bones were ready to creep one into another, for fear of an operation.

Then came a set of people, whom, by their dress, I should have taken for devils in disguise, if I had not spied their chains of rotten teeth, which put me in some hope they might be tooth-drawers; and so they proved. This is one of the lewdest trades in the world; for they are good for nothing but to depopulate our mouths, and make us old before our time. Let a man but yawn, and you shall have one of these rogues examining his grinders; and there is not a sound tooth in your head, but he had rather see it at his girdle, than in the place of its nativity; nay, rather than fail, he will pick a quarrel with your gums. But that which puts me out of all patience, is to see these scoundrels ask twice as much for drawing an old tooth, as would have bought me a new one.

I now said to myself, we are now past the worst, unless the devil himself come next : and in that instant I heard the brushing of guitars, and the rattling of citterns, raking over certain allegros and sarabands. These are a kennel of barbers, thought I, or I will be hanged; and any man that had ever seen a barber's shop, might have told you as much without a conjuror, both by the music, and by the very instruments, which are as proper a part of a barber's furniture, as his comb-cases and wash-bowls. It was droll enough to see them lathering asses' heads, of all sorts and sizes, and their customers all the while winking and spluttering over their basins. Presently, after these, appeared a concert of loud and tedious talkers, that tired and deafened the company with their shrill and constant babbling. These were of various kinds; some they called swimmers, from the motion of their arms in all their discourses, which was just as if they had been paddling. Others they call apes, or mimics. These were perpetually making faces, and a thousand antic, foolish gestures, in derision and imitation of others. In the third place were sowers of dissension; and these were still rolling their eyes like a Bartlemy puppet, without so much as moving the head, and leering over their shoulders, to surprise people at unawares in their familiarities and privacies, and gather matter for calumny and detraction. Liars followed next; and these seemed to be a jolly, contented sort of people, well fed and well clothed; and having nothing else to trust to, methought it was a strange trade to live upon. I need not tell you that they always have a full audience, since their congregation consists of all the fools and impertinents.

After these came a company of meddlers; a pragmatical, insolent generation of men, that will have an oar in every boat, and are, indeed, the bane of honest conversation, and the pest of all companies. Then came the most prostitute of all, I mean flatterers, who were only devoted to their own profit. I thought this had been the last scene, because no more came upon the stage for a considerable time; and indeed I wondered that they came so late; but one of the babblers told me, unasked, that this kind of serpent, carrying his venom in his tail, it seemed reasonable, that being the most poisonous of the whole gang, they should bring up the rear.

I then began to consider what might be the meaning of this olio of people, of several conditions and humours met together; but I was presently diverted from that consideration, by the apparition of a creature, which looked as if it were of the feminine gender. It was a person of a thin and slender make, laden with crowns, garlands, sceptres, scythes, sheep-hooks, pattens, hob-nailed shoes, tiaras, straw hats, mitres, caps, embroideries, skins, silk, wool, gold, lead, diamonds, shells, pearl and pebbles. She was dressed up in all the colours of the rainbow; she had one eye shut, the other open; young on the one side, and old on the other. I thought at first she had been at a great distance, when indeed she was very near me; and when I took her to be at my chamber-door, she was at my bed's head. How to unriddle this mystery I knew not; nor was it possible for me to understand the meaning of an equipage so extravagant, and so fantastically put together. It gave me no fright, however; but, on the contrary, I could not forbear laughing; for it came just into my mind, that I had formerly seen, in Italy, a farce where the mimic, pretending to come from the infernal regions, was just thus accoutred; and never was anything more nonsensically pleasant. I held as long as I could, and at last I asked what she was? She answered, "I am Death." Death! the very word made me tremble: I beseech you, Madam, said I, with great humility and respect, whither is your honour going? No farther, said she, for now I have found you I am at my journey's end. Alas! and must I die then? said I. No, no, replied Death, but I will take thee alive along with me: for since so many of the dead have been to visit the living, it is but equal, for once, that one of the living should return a visit to the dead. Get up, then, and come along, without reluctance; for what you will not do willingly, you shall do in spite of your teeth. This put me in a cold fit; but, without more delay, up I started, and desired leave to put on my breeches. No, no, said she, no matter for clothes, no body wears them upon this road: Come away, naked as you are, and you will travel the better. So up I got, without saying any more, and followed her, in such a terror and amazement, that I was in an ill condition to take a strict account of my passage; yet I remember, upon the way, that I told her that under correction, she was no more like the Deaths I had seen, than a horse is like a cat: Our Death, I said, was represented with a scythe in her hand, and a carcass of bones, as clean as if the crows had picked it. Yes, yes, said she, turning short upon me, I know that very well; but, in the meantime, your designers and painters are but a parcel of blockheads. The bones you talk of, are the dead, or, otherwise, the miserable remainders of the living; but let me tell you, that you yourselves make your own death; and that which you call death, is but the period of your life, as the first moment of your birth is the beginning of your existence: And, actually you die living, and your bones are no more than what Death has left, and committed to the grave. If this were rightly understood, every man would find a *memento mori*, or a Death's head, in his own looking-glass; and consider every house with a family in it, but as a sepulchre filled with dead bodies; a truth which you little dream of, though within your daily view and experience.

Can you imagine a Death elsewhere, and not in yourselves? Believe it, you are greatly mistaken; for you yourselves are skeletons before you know anything of the matter.

But pray, Madam, cried I, what may all these people be that keep your ladyship company? And since you are Death, as you say, what is the reason that the babblers and the slanderers are nearer your person, and more in your graces than the physicians? Why, replied she, there are more people talked to death, and despatched by babblers, than by all the pestilential diseases in the world. And then, your slanderers and meddlers kill more than your physicians; though (to give the gentlemen of the faculty their due) they labour perpetually for the enlargement of our empire: For you must understand, that though distempered humours make a man sick, it is the physician kills him; and he expects to be well paid for it too; and it is fit that every man should live by his trade. So that, when a man is asked what such and such a one died of, he is not presently to make answer, that he died of a fever, a pleurisy, the plague, or the palsy, but that he died of the doctor. In one point, however, I must needs acquit the physician: You know that the style honourable and worshipful, which was heretofore appropriated only to persons of eminent degree and quality, is, nowadays, used by all degrees of people; nay, the very bare-foot friars, that live under vows of humility and mortification, are stung with this itch of title and vain glory. Your ordinary tradesmen, as vintners, tailors and masons, must be all dressed up, forsooth, in the worshipful; whereas, your physician does not so much court honour: Even if it should rain dignities, he would scarce be persuaded to venture the wetting; but sits down contented with the honour of disposing of your lives and money, without troubling himself about any other reputation.

The entertainment of these lectures and discourses made the way seem short and agreeable; and we were just now entering into a place, but barely illuminated, and of horror enough, if Death and I had not, by this time, been very well acquainted. Upon one side of the passage I saw three moving spectres, armed, and of human shape, and so like each other that I could not say which was which. Just opposite, on the other side, was a dreadful monster, in a fierce and obstinate combat with these. Here Death made a stop, and facing about, asked me if I knew these people? Alas! no, said I; Heaven be praised I do not; and I shall put it in my Litany, that I never may. How ignorant thou art! cried Death; these are thy old acquaintance, and thou hast hardly ever kept any other company since thou wert born. Those three are the World, the Flesh and the

Devil, the capital enemies of thy soul: And they so much resemble each other, as well in quality as appearance, that effectually, whoever has one, has all. The proud and ambitious man thinks he has got the World, but it proves the Devil. The lecher and the epicure persuade themselves that they have gotten the Flesh, but that is the Devil too; and, in a word, thus it fares with all other kinds of extravagants. But what is here, said I, that appears in such various shapes, and fights against the other three? That, replied Death, is the Devil of Money, who maintains that he himself alone is equivalent to the three, and that whenever he comes, there is no need of them. Against the World, he urges from its own confession: For it passes for an oracle, that there is no world but money. He that is out of money, is out of the world. Take away a man's money, and take away his life. Money answers all things. Against the second enemy, he pleads that money is the flesh too; witness the girls and Ganymedes it procures and maintains. And against the third he urges that there is nothing to be done without money. Love does much, but money does everything: And money will make the pot to boil, though the devil piss in the fire. So that, for ought I see, said I, the Devil of Money has the better end of the staff.

After this, advancing a little farther, I beheld on the one hand Judgment, and Hell on the other, for so Death called them. Making a stop, upon the sight of Hell, to view it more narrowly. Death asked me what it was I looked at. I told her it was Hell; and I was the more intent upon it, because I thought I had seen it somewhere else before. She asked me, where? I told her that I had seen it in the corruption and avarice of wicked magistrates; in the pride and haughtiness of courtiers; in the appetites of the voluptuous; in the lewd designs of Ruin and Revenge ; in the souls of oppressors ; and in the vanity of princes. But he that would see it whole and entire, in one subject, must examine the hypocrite, who is a kind of religious broker, and puts out at five-and-forty per cent. the very sacraments and the ten commandments.

I am very well pleased too, said I, that I have seen Judgment, as I find it here, in its purity; for that which we call judgment in the world, is a mere mockery: If it were like this, men would live in another manner than they do. If it be expected that our judges should govern themselves and us by this Judgment, the world is in an ill case, for there is but little of it there: And to deal plainly, as matters are, I have no great inclination to go home again; for it is better being with the dead, where there is justice, than with the living, where there is none.

We next went into a fair and spacious plain, environed with a high wall, where he that is once in, must never expect to get out again. Stop here, cried Death, for we are now come to my judgment-seat, and here it is that I give audience.

The walls were hung with sighs and groans, ill-news, fears, doubts and surprises. Tears did not there avail either the lover or the beggar; but grief and care were without both measure and comfort, and served as vermin, to gnaw the hearts of emperors and princes, feeding upon the insolent and ambitious, as their proper food. I saw Envy there, dressed up in a widow's veil, and the very picture of the governante of one of our noblemen's houses. She kept a continual fast as to the shambles, preying only upon herself, and could not but be very thin upon so mean a diet. Nothing came amiss to her teeth, good or bad, which made them yellow and rotten; and the reason was, that though she bit, and set her mark upon the good and sound, she could never swallow it. Under her sat her daughter Discord. She had formerly conversed with married people; but, finding no need of her assistance there, away she went to colleges and corporations, where, it seems, they had more already than they knew what to do with. Then she took herself to courts and palaces, and officiated there as the Devil's vicegerent. Next to her was Ingratitude; and she, out of a certain paste, made up of pride and malice, was moulding of new devils. I was very much delighted at this discovery, being of opinion, till now, that the ungrateful had been the devils themselves; because I read, that the angels which fell were made devils for their ingratitude. In short, the whole place echoed with rage and curses. What a devil have we here to do, said I; does it rain curses in this country? Upon which a devil at my elbow asked me what a devil could I expect else, in a place where there were so many match-makers, attorneys, and common barreters, who were a pack of the most villainous wretches in nature? Is there anything more common in the world than these exclamations of husbands and wives? Oh! that damned devil of a pander: A curse upon that bitch of a bawd that ever brought us together. The pillory and ten thousand gibbets take that pick-pocket attorney, that advised me to this law-suit; he has undone me for ever? But pray, said I, what do all these match-makers and attorneys do here together? Do they come for audience? Death was here a little quick upon me, and called me a blockhead for so impertinent a question. If there were no match-makers, said she, we should not have the tenth part of these skeletons and desperadoes. Am not I here, the fifth husband of a woman yet living in the world, that hopes to send twice as many more after me, and drink to be drunk at the fifteenth's funeral? You say well, said I, as to the business of match-makers; but prithee, why so many pettifoggers? Nay, then I see, cried Death, now you have a mind to seize me; for that devilish kind of caterpillars have been my undoing. Had not a man better die by the common hangman, than by the hand of an attorney; to be killed by falsities, quirks, cavils, delays, exceptions, cheats, and circumventions? Yes, yes, and it must not be denied, that these makers of matches, and splitters of causes, are the principal support of this imperial throne.

At these words I raised my eyes, and saw Death seated in her chair of state, with a multitude of little Deaths crowding about her; as the Death of Love, of Cold, Hunger, Fear and Laughter; all with their several ensigns and devices. The Death of Love, I perceived, had very little brain, and, to keep herself in countenance, kept company with Pyramus and Thisbe, Hero and Leander, and Amadis and Palmerin, d'Oliva; all embalmed, steeped in good vinegar, and well dried. I saw several other kinds of lovers too, that were brought, in all appearance, to their last agonies; but, by the singular miracle of self-interest, recovered to the tune of

> *Will, if looking well won't move her,*
> *Looking ill prevail?*

The Death of Cold was attended by several prelates, bishops, abbots, and other ecclesiastics, who had neither wives nor children, nor indeed anybody else that cared for them, farther than for their fortunes. These, when they came to a fit of sickness, were stripped even to their sheets and bedding, before they could say Paternoster: Nay, frequently they were pillaged, ere they were laid; and destroyed, for want of clothes to keep them warm.

The Death of Hunger was surrounded with a vast number of avaricious misers, that were cording up trunks, bolting doors and windows, locking up cellars and garrets, nailing down trap-doors, burying pots of money, and starting at every breath of wind they heard. Their eyes were ready to drop out of their heads, for want of sleep; their mouths and bellies complained of their hands; and their souls turned into gold and silver, the idols they adored.

The Death of Fear had the most magnificent train and attendance of all the rest, being accompanied with a great multitude of usurpers and tyrants, who commonly do justice upon themselves, for the injuries they have done to others: Their own consciences doing the office of tormenters, and avenging their public

C

crimes, by their private sufferings, for they live in a continual anguish of thought, with fears and jealousies.

The Death of Laughter was the last of all, and surrounded with a vast concourse of people, hasty to believe, and slow to repent; living without hope of mercy. These are they that pay all their debts and duties with a jest. Bid any of them give every man his due, and return what he has either borrowed or wrongfully taken, and his answer is, You'd make a man burst his sides with laughing. Tell him, my friend, you are now in years, your dancing days are done, and your body is worn out, what should such a scarecrow as you are, do with a bed-fellow? Give over your bawdy haunts, for shame, nor make a glory of sin, when you are past the pleasures of it. This fellow, says he, would make a man die with laughing. Come, come, say your prayers, and bethink yourself of eternity; you have one foot in the grave already, and it is high time to fit yourself for the other world. Thou wilt absolutely kill me with laughing. I tell thee, I am as sound as a roach, and I do not remember that ever I was better in my life. Others there are that let a man advise them upon their death-beds, and even at their last gasp, to send for a divine, or to make some handsome settlement of their estates; Alas! alas! they will cry, I have frequently been as bad as before and, I hope, in the Lord, there is no need to think of him yet. These men are lost for ever, before they can be brought to understand their danger. This vision wrought strangely upon me, and gave me all the pains and marks imaginable of a true repentance. Well, said I, since it is so, that man has but one life allotted him, and so many deaths; but one way into the world, and so many millions out of it; I will certainly, at my return, make it more my care than it has been, to live with a good conscience, that I may die with comfort.

I had hardly done with speaking, before the crier of the court, with a loud voice called out, The dead, the dead; let the dead appear. Immediately I saw the earth begin to move, and gently opening itself, to make way, first for heads and arms, and then by degrees for the whole bodies of men and women, that came out, half muffled in their night-caps, and ranged themselves in excellent order, and profound silence. Now, says Death, let everyone speak in his turn; and, in the instant, up comes one of the dead to my very beard, with so much fury and boldness in his face and action, that I would have given him half the teeth in my head for a composition. These devils of the world, cried he, what would they be at? My masters, cannot a poor wretch be quiet in his grave for ye, but ye must be railing at him, and charging him with things that, upon my soul, he is as innocent of as the child that is unborn? What hurt has he done any of you, ye rescals, to be thus abused? I beseech you, Sir, said I under your favour, who may you be, as I confess I have not the honour either to know or understand you? I am replied he, the unfortunate buffoon that has been dead now this many a fair year, and yet your wife worships, forsooth, have not wit enough to make yourselves and your company merry, but I must still be one half of the entertainment. When any man plays the fool or the extravagant, presently he is a buffoon. Who drew this or that ridiculous piece? The buffoon. Such or such a one was never well taught: No, he had a buffoon to his master. But let me tell you, he that shall call your wisdoms to task, and take a strict account of your words and actions, will, upon the upshot, find you are all nothing but buffoons; and, in effect, even greater impertinents. For instance, did I ever make ridiculous wills, as you do, to oblige others to pray for a man in his grave, that never prayed in his life? Did I ever rebel against my superiors? Or, was I ever so errant a coxcomb, as, by colouring my cheeks and hair, to imagine I could reform nature, and make myself young again? Can you say that ever I put an oath to a lie, or broke a solemn promise, as you do daily! Did I ever enslave myself to money; or, on the other hand, squander it away? Did my wife ever wear the breeches? Or, did I ever marry at all, to be revenged of a false mistress? Was I ever so very an idiot, as to believe any man would be true to me, who had betrayed his friend? or, to venture all my hopes upon the wheel of Fortune? Did I ever envy the happiness of a court-life, that sells and spends all for a glance? What pleasure did I ever take in the profane discourses of heretics and libertines? or, did I ever lift myself in the party of enthusiasts, to get the name of a gifted brother? Whoever saw me insolent to my inferiors, or basely servile to my betters? Did I ever go to a conjurer, or to your dealers of nativities and horoscopes, upon any occasion of loss or death? Now, if yourselves be guilty of all these fopperies, and I innocent, I beseech you where is the fool? So that you see the buffoon is not the buffoon you imagine he is: But to crown his other virtues, he is also endued with so large a stock of patience, that whosoever needed it, had it for the asking; unless it were such as came to borrow money; or, in cases of women that claimed marriage of him; or valets that would be making sport of his bauble; and to these he was as resolute as John Florio.

During this discourse, another of the dead came marching up to me, with a Spanish face and gravity; and giving me a touch with his elbow, Look in my face, cried he, with a stern countenance, and know, Sir, that you are not to have to do with a fool. I beseech your Lordship, replied I, let me know your honour, that I may pay my respects accordingly; for I must own I thought all people here had been, Hail fellow, well met. Mortals, answered he, call me Queen Bess; and whether you know me or not, I am sure you think and talk of me often enough; and if the devil did not possess you, you would let the dead alone, and content yourselves to prosecute one another. You cannot see a high-crowned hat, a threadbare cloak, a basket-hilt sword, or a dudgeon dagger, nay, not so much as a reverend matron well advanced in years, but presently you cry, this or that is in the mode, or date of Queen Bess. If you were not, every mother's child of you, stark mad, you would confess that Queen Bess's were golden days, to those you have had since; and it is an easy matter to prove what I say. Will you see a mother now teaching her daughter a lesson of good government? Child, says she, you know that modesty is the chief ornament of your sex; wherefore, be sure, when you come into company, that you do not stand staring the men in the face, as if you were looking babies in their eyes; but rather look a little downwards, as a fashion of behaviour more suitable to the obligations of your sex. Downward! says the girl, I must beg to be excused, Madam. This was well enough in the days of Queen Bess, when the poor creatures knew no better. Let the men look downward towards the clay of which they were made; but man was our original, and it becomes us to keep our eyes upon the matter from whence we came. If a father charges his son to worship his Creator; to say his prayers morning and evening; to give thanks before and after meat; to avoid gaming and swearing, you shall have the son make answer; that it is true this was practised in the time of Queen Bess, but it is now quite out of mode; and, in a word, that men are better known now-adays, by their atheism and blasphemy, than by their beards.

Thus saying, Queen Bess withdrew, and then appeared a large glass bottle, wherein was enclosed, as I heard, a famous necromancer, hacked and minced, according to his own order, to render him immortal. It was boiling upon a quick fire; and the flesh, by little and little, began to piece again, and made, first an arm, then a thigh, after that a leg, and, at last, there was an entire body, that raised itself upright in the bottle. Bless me, thought I, what is here! a man made out of pottage, and brought into the world out of the belly of a bottle. This vision greatly terrified me; and, while I was yet panting and trembling, a voice was heard out of the glass: In what year of our Lord are we? One thousand six hundred and thirty-six, replied I: Then be it welcome, said he, for it is the happy year I have so much wished for. And who is he,

I pray, quoth I, that I now see and hear in the belly of the bottle? I am, said he, the great necromancer of Europe; and certainly you cannot but have heard both of my operations in general, and of this particular design. I have heard talk of you from a child, said I; but all those stories I only took for old wives' fables. You are the man then, it seems: I must confess, that, at first, at a distance, I took this bottle for the vessel that the ingenious Rabelais makes mention of; but coming near enough to see what was in it, I then did imagine it might be some philosopher by fire, or some apothecary doing penance for his errors. To tell you the truth, it has cost me many a heavy step to come hither; and yet, to see so great a curiosity, I cannot but think my time and pains very well bestowed. The necromancer called to me then to unstop the bottle; and, as I was breaking the clay to open it, Hold, hold a little, cried he, prithee tell me first, how go affairs in Spain? What money, force, credit? The Plate-fleets go and come, said I, reasonably well; but foreigners that come in for their shares, have half-spoiled the trade. The Genoese run out as far as the mountain of Potosi, and have almost drained them dry. My child, cried he, that trade can never be secure and open, so long as Spain has an enemy that is potent at sea. And for the Genoese, they will tell you this is no injustice at all, but, on the contrary, a new way of quitting old scores, and justifying his Catholic Majesty for a good pay-master. I am no enemy to that nation, but upon the account of their vices and encroachments; and, I confess, rather than see those villains prosper, I would turn myself into a jelly again, as you saw me just now; nay, I did not care if it were into a powder, though I ended my days in a tobacco-box. Good Sir, replied I, comfort yourself, for these people are as miserable as you could wish them. You know they are cavaliers and signiors already; and now, they have an itch upon them to be princes: a vanity that gnaws them like a cancer; and by drawing on great expenses, breeds a worm in their traffic; so that you will find little but debt and extravagance at the foot of the account. And then the devil is in them for a wench; insomuch, that it is well if they make both ends meet; for what is gotten upon the 'Change is spent in the Stews.

This is well, cried the necromancer, and I am glad to hear it. Pray, tell me now what price bears honour and honesty in the world? There is much to be said, answered I, upon that point; but, in brief, there was never more of it in talk, nor less in effect. Upon my honesty, cries the tradesman; upon my honour, says his lordship: and, in a word, every man has it, and everything is it, in some disguise or other; but, duly considered there is no such thing upon earth. The thief says it is more honourable to take than beg. He that asks an

alms pleads that it is honester to beg than steal. Nay, false witnesses and murderers themselves stand upon their punctilios as well as their neighbours, and
will tell you, that a man of honour will rather be buried alive than submit;
though they will not always do as they say. In a word, every man sets up a
court of honour within himself; pronounces everything honourable that serves
his purpose, and laughs at them who are of a different opinion. To say the
truth, all things are now topsy-turvy. A good faculty in lying is a fair step to
preferment; and, to pack a game at cards, or cog a die, is become the mark
and glory of a cavalier. The Spaniards formerly were, I confess, a very coura-
geous and well-governed people; but they have evil tongues among them now-
adays, that they might even go to school to the Indians, to learn sobriety and
virtue. They are not really sober, but at their own tables; which, indeed, is
rather avarice than moderation; for, when they eat or drink at another man's
cost, there are no greater gluttons in the world; and, for fuddling, they will
outdo the best pot-companion in Switzerland.

The necromancer went on with his discourse, and asked me what number
of lawyers and attorneys were in Spain at present? I told him that the whole
world swarmed with them, and that there were abundance of all sorts; some
by profession, others by intrusion and presumption, and some again by study,
but not many of the last; though, indeed, sufficient of every kind to make the
people pray for the Egyptian locusts and caterpillars, in exchange for such
vermin. Why then, replied the necromancer, if there be such plagues abroad, I
think I had best e'en keep where I am. It is with justice, said I, as with sick
men; in times past, when we had fewer doctors, as well of law as of physic, we
had more right, and more health; but we are now destroyed by multitudes and
consultations, which serve to no other end than to inflame both the distemper
and the reckoning. Justice, as well as Truth, went naked in ancient times; one
single book of laws and ordinances was enough for the best ordered government
in the universe; but the justice of our age is tricked up with bills, parchments,
writs and labels; and furnished with abundance of codes, digests, pandects,
pleadings, and reports; and what is their use, but to make wrangling a science,
and to embroil us in seditions, suits, and endless trouble and confusion? We
have had more books published this last twenty years than in a thousand before;
and there hardly passes a term without a new author, in four or five volumes at
least, under the titles of glosses, commentaries, cases or judgments. The great
strife is now, who writes most, not best; so that the whole bulk is but a body
without a soul, and fitter for a churchyard than a study. In a word, these

lawyers and solicitors are but so many smoke-merchants, sellers of wind, and troublers of the public peace. If there were no attorneys, there would be no suits; if no suits, no cheats; no serjeants, no catchpoles, no prisons; if no prisons, no judges; no judges, no passion; no passion, no bribery or subordination.

See now what prodigious multitudes of mischief one wretched pettifogger draws after him! If you go to him for counsel, he hears your story, reads your case, and tells you very gravely, Sir, this is a nice point, and should be well handled; we will see what the law says. And then he runs over with his eye and finger a matter of a hundred volumes, grumbling all the while like a cat, that claws in her play, betwixt jest and earnest. At last, down comes the book; he shows the law, bids you leave your papers, and he will study the question. But your case is very good, by what I see already; and if you will come again in the evening, or tomorrow morning, I will tell you more. But pardon me, Sir, now I think on it, I am retained upon another business, it cannot be till Monday next, and then I am at your service. When you are to part, and that you are come to the giving him his fee, the best thing in the world both for the wit and memory, Good lord, Sir, says he, what do you mean? I beseech you, Sir; nay, pray Sir; and if he spies you drawing back the paw opens, seizes the gold, and good-morrow dupe. Sayest thou so? cried the good fellow in the glass; stop me up close again, as thou lovest me; for the very air of these rascals will poison me, if ever I put my head out of this bottle till the whole race of them be extinct. In the interim, take this for a rule, He that would thrive by law, must see his enemy's counsel as well as his own.

But now you talk of great cheats, what news of the Venetians? Is Venice still in the world or no? In the world, do you say, replied I? yes, indeed it is, and stands just where it did. Why then, said he, prithee give it to the devil, from me, as a token of my love; for it is a present equal to the severest revenge. Nothing can ever destroy that republic but conscience; and then you will say, it is like to be long-lived; for if every man had his own, it would not be left worth a groat. In short, it is an odd kind of commonwealth; it is the very anus, the drain and sink of monarchies, both in war and peace. It helps the Turks to vex the Christians, and the Christians to gall the Turks; and maintains itself to torment both. The inhabitants are neither Moors nor Christians, as appears by a Venetian captain, in a combat against a Christin enemy. Stand to it, my soldiers, says he to his men; you were Venetians before you were Christians.

Enough, enough of this, cried the necromancer, and tell me how stand the people affected? what malcontents and mutineers? Mutiny, said I, is so universal a disease that every kingdom is but, in effect, a great hospital, or rather a bedlam; for all men are mad, to entertain the disaffected. There is no stirring for me, then, cried the necromancer; but pray commend me, however, to those busy fools, and tell them that, carry what face they will, there is vanity and ambition in the bottom. Kings and princes very much resemble quick-silver; they are in perpetual agitation, and without any repose. Press them too hard, that is to say, beyond the bounds of duty and reason, and they are lost. You may observe that your gilders, and great dealers in quick-silver, are generally troubled with the palsy; and so should all subjects tremble, that have to do with majesty; and better to do it at first out of respect, than afterwards by force and necessity.

But, before I fall to pieces again, as you saw me just now, for better so than worse, I beseech you, one word more, and then I am done: Who is King of Spain at present? You know, said I, that Philip the Third is dead: Right, replied he; a prince of incomparable piety and virtue, or my stars deceive me. After him, said I, came Philip the Fourth. If it be so, cried he, break, break my bottle immediately and help me out; for I am resolved to try my fortune in the world once again, under the reign of that inestimable prince. And with that word, he dashed the glass in pieces against a rock, crept out of his case, and away he ran. I had a good mind to have kept him company; but as I was just about to start, Let him go, let him go, cried one of the dead, and laid hold of my arm, he has devilish heels, and you will never come up with him.

Upon this I stayed; and what should I see next, but a wondrous old man, whose name might have been Bucephalus, by his head, and the hair on his face might well have stuffed a couple of cushions; take him together, and you will find his picture in the map among the savages. I need not tell you that I stared upon him sufficiently; which he taking notice of, came to me, and said, Friend, my spirit tells me that you are now in pain to know who I am; know, therefore, that my name is Nostrodamus. Are you the author then, said I, of that medley of prophecies that is published in your name? Medley, dost thou say? replied he: Impudent and cruel rascal, to despise mysteries that are above thy reach, and to revile the secretary of the stars, and the interpreter of the destinies. Who is so brutal as to doubt the meaning of those lines which I composed?

> *From second causes this I gather,*
> *Nought shall befall us, good or ill,*
> *Either upon the land or water,*
> *But what the Great Disposer will.*

Wretched and foolish rascals that ye are, what greater blessing could betide the world, than the accomplishment of this prophecy? Would it not establish justice and holiness, and suppress all the absurd suggestions and motions of the devil? Men would not then any longer set their hearts upon avarice, fraud, and extortion, and make money their god; that vagabond, Money, that is trotting up and down like a wandering whore, and takes up most commonly with the unworthy, leaving the philosophers and prophets, who are the very oracles of the heavens, such as Nostrodamus, to go barefoot. But let us go on with our prophecies, and see if they be so frivolous and dark as they are said to be.

When the married shall marry,
Then the jealous will be sorry;
And though fools will be talking,
To keep their tongues walking,
No man runs well I find,
But with's elbows behind.

I could not refrain from laughing when he said this, which put him out of all patience. Buffoon and dog-whelp, as you are, cried he, there is a bone for you to pick; you must be snarling and snapping at everything. Will your teeth serve you now to fetch out the marrow of this prophecy? Hear then, in the devil's name, and be mannerly; hear, and learn, I say; and let us have no more of that grinning, unless you have a mind to leave your beard behind you. Do you imagine that all that are married, marry? No, not the one half of them. When you are married, the priest has done his part; but, after that, to marry is to do the duty of a husband. Alas! how many married men live as if they were single! and how many bachelors, on the other side, as if they were married! after the mode of the times. And wedlock, to many couples, is no other than a most sociable state of virginity. Here is one half of my prophecy expounded already; now for the rest. Let me see you run a little for experiment, and try if you can carry your elbows before or behind. You will tell me, perhaps, that this is speaking foolishly, because everybody knows it. A pleasant shift; as if truth were the worse for being plain. The things, indeed, that you deliver for truths, are generally mere fooleries and mistakes; and it were a hard matter to put truth in such a dress as would please you. What have you to say now, either against my prophecy or my argument? Not a syllable, I warrant you, and yet somewhat there is to be said; for there is no rule without an exception. Does not the

physician carry his elbow before him, when he puts back his hand to take his
patient's money? and away he is gone in a trice, as soon as he has made his
purchase. But, to proceed, I shall tell you another of my prophecies:

> *Many women shall be mothers,*
> *And their babbies*
> *Their own daddies.*

What say you to this now? Are there not many husbands, do you think,
if the truth were known, that father more children than their own?
Believe me, friend, a man had need have good security upon a woman's
belly; for children are commonly got in the dark, and it is no easy matter to
know the workman, especially having nothing but the woman's bare word for
it. This is meant of the Court of Assistance; and, whoever interprets my
prophecies, to the prejudice of any person of honour, does me injustice. You
little think what a world of our gay folks, in their coaches and six, with their
valets at their heels, by the dozens will be found, at the last day, to be only the
bastards of pages, gentlemen ushers, or valet-de-chambres of the family; nay,
perhaps the physician may have his hand in the wrong box; and, in case of
a necessity, good use has been made of a lusty coachman. Little do you think,
I say, how many noble families, upon that grand discovery, will be found extinct
for want of issue.

I am now fully convinced, said I to the mathematician, of the excellency
of your predictions; and I perceive, since you have been pleased to be your own
interpreter, that they have more weight in them than we imagined. You shall
have one more, said he, and I have done.

> *This year, if I've any skill i' th' weather,*
> *Shall many a one take wing with a feather.*

You will undoubtedly now imagine that I am talking of rooks and jackdaws; but I say, no; I speak of lawyers, attorneys, clerks, scriveners, and their
fellows; that with the dash of a pen can rob their clients of their estates, and
fly away with them when they have done.

Thus saying, Nostrodamus vanished; and, somebody plucking me behind,
I turned my face upon the most meagre, melancholic wretch that ever was seen,
and clothed in white. For pity's sake, says he, and as you are a good Christian,

do but deliver me from the persecution of these impertinents and babblers, that are now tormenting me, and I will be eternally obliged to you; casting himself at my feet, at the same moment, and crying like a child. And what art thou, said I? For a miserable creature I am sure thou art! I am, says he, an ancient and an honest man, although defamed with a thousand reproaches. Some call me another, and others, somebody; and, doubtless, you cannot but have heard of me; as somebody says, cries one, that has nothing to say for himself; and yet I never so much as opened my mouth before. The Latins call me *quidam;* and make good use of me to fill up lines and stop gaps. When you go back again into the world, I pray do me the favour to own that you have seen me; and to justify me for one that never did, and never will, either speak or write anything, whatever some tattling idiots may pretend. When they bring me into quarrels and brawls, I am called, forsooth, a certain person; in their intrigues, I know not who; and, in the pulpit, a certain author. And all this to make a mystery of my name, and lay all their fooleries at my door. Wherefore, I beseech you, lend me all the assistance in your power; which I promised to do; and so this phantom withdrew, to make place for another.

This was the most dreadful piece of antiquity that ever eye beheld, in the shape of an old woman. She came nodding towards me; and in a hollow rattling tone (for she spoke more with her chops than her tongue), pray, says she, is there not somebody come lately here from the other world? This apparition, thought I, must certainly be one of the devil's scarecrows. Her eyes were so sunk in their sockets that they looked like a pair of dice in the bottom of a couple of red boxes. Her cheeks, and the soles of her feet, were of the same complexion. Her mouth was pale and open, the better to receive the distillations of her nose. Her chin was covered with a kind of goosedown; and the flaps of her cheeks were like an ape's bags. Her head danced; and her voice at every word kept time to it. Her body was veiled, or rather wrapped up in a shroud of crepe. She had a crutch in one hand, which served her for a supporter; and a rosary in the other, of such a length that as she was stepping over it, a man would have thought she had been fishing for death's heads. When I had done gaping upon this epitome of past ages, Ho! grannum, shouted I in her ear, imagining that she was deaf, what is your pleasure with me? With that she gave a groan, and being very angry at being called grannum, clapt a pair of spectacles upon her nose, and prying through them, I am, cried she, neither deaf nor grannum, but may be called by my name, as well as my neighbours; giving to understand that women do not love to be called old, even in their very graves. As she spoke, she came still nearer me, with her eyes dropping, and with a cadaveron smell. I begged her pardon for what was past, and asked her name, that I might be sure to keep myself within the bounds of respect. I am called, says she, Douegna, or Madam la Gouvernante. What, cried I, in great amazement, have you any of those cattle in this country? Let the inhabitants pray heartily for peace then; and all little enough to keep them quiet. But see how much I have been mistaken; I thought the women had not died when they came to be gouvernantes; and that for the punishment of a wicked world, the gouvernantes had been immortal: But I am now better informed, and very glad, truly, to meet with a person I have heard so much talk of: For with us, who but Madam la Gouvernante is constantly in our mouths? Do you see that mumping hag, cries one? Come here, you vile jade, cries another. That old bawd, says a third, has forgotten, I warrant you, that ever she was a whore. And now see if we do not remember you? You do so, and I am in your debt for your remembrance; the great devil be your paymaster, you son of a whore, you; are there no more gouvernantes than myself? Sure there are; and you may have your choice, without affronting me. Well, well, said I, have a little patience, and at my return I will endeavour to put things in better order; but, in the meantime, what business have you here? Her reverence, upon this, was a little mollified, and told me that she had now been eight hundred years in hell, upon a design to erect an order of gouvernantes; but the right worshipful the devil-commissioners were not, as yet, come to any resolution upon the point. For, say they, if your gouvernantes should settle here, there would need no other tormentors; and we should have nothing to do. And besides, we should be perpetually at daggers-drawing, about the faggots and candle-ends; which they would still be filching, and laying out of the way; and for us to have our fuel to seek, would be very inconvenient. I have been in Purgatory, too, said she, upon the same project; but there, as soon as ever they beheld me, all the souls cried out unanimously, What a monster! As for Heaven, that is no place for quarrels, slanders, disquiets, heart-burnings; and consequently none for me. The dead are none of my friends neither; for they grumble, and bid me let them alone, and order me to be gone into the world again if I please; and there, they tell me, I may play the gouvernante from one generation to another. But truly I had rather be here at my ease than spend my life crumpling and brooding over a carpet, at a bedside, like a stick dressed up with clouts, to secure the poultry of the family from strange cocks, which would now and then have a brush with a virgin pullet, but for the care of the gouvernante. And yet it is she, good woman, that bears all the blame;

in case of any miscarriage, the gouvernante was presently of the plot; she had
a feeling in the cause, a finger in the pie : And, in short, she must be answerable
for all. Let but a sock, an old handkerchief, the greasy lining of a mask, or any
such frippery piece of business be missing; ask the gouvernante for it. In short,
they take us certainly for so many storks and ducks, to gather up all the filth
about the house. The servants look upon us as spies and tell-tales; this one's
cousin, forsooth, and that's aunt dare not come to the house for fear of the
gouvernante. And indeed I have made many of them cross themselves that took
me for a ghost. We are cursed by our masters, too, for embroiling the family. So
that I have rather chosen to take up here betwixt the dead and the living than
to return again into my charge of a douegna, the very sound of the name being
more terrible than a gibbet; as appears by one that was lately travelling from
Madrid to Valadolid, and asking where he might lodge that night, answer was
made, at a small village called Douegnas. But is there no other place, cried
he, within some reasonable distance, not so far, or beyond it? They told him,
no; unless it were under the gibbet. That shall be my quarters then, replied he;
for a thousand gibbets are not so bad to me as one douegna. Now you see how
we are abused, said the gouvernante; I hope you will do us some right when
it lies in your power.

She would have talked me to death, if I had not fled from her, upon
removing of her spectacles : But I could not escape so neither; for looking about
me for a guide to carry me home again, I was arrested by one of the dead : A
good proper fellow, only he had a pair of ram's horns on his head; and I was
about to salute him for Aries in the Zodiac, when I saw him plant himself just
before me, with his best leg forward, stretching out his arms, clutching his fists,
and looking as sour as if he would have swallowed me : Doubtless, said I, the
the devil is dead, and this is he. No, no, cried a bystander, this is a man. Why
then, said I, I perceive he is drunk, and quarrelsome in his liquor, for there is
nobody has touched him. With that, as he was just ready to fall on, I stood to
my guard, and we were armed at all points alike, only he had the odds of the
headpiece. Now, sirrah, says he, have at you; slave that you are, to make a
trade of defaming persons of honour. By the Death that reigns here, I will
have my revenge and turn your skin over your ears. This insolent language, I
must own, enraged me, and so I called to him, Come on, sirrah; a little nearer
yet; and, if you have a mind to be twice killed, I will do your business; who the
devil brought this cuckold hither to trouble me? No sooner had I said this, than
we were immediately at it, tooth and nail; and if his horns had not been flatted

to his head, I might have had the worst of it. But the whole ring presently came in to part us, and did me a singular kindness in it, for my adversary had a fork, and I had none. As they were running about us, You might have had more manners, cried one, than to give such language to your betters, and to call Don Diego Moreno cuckold. And is this that Diego Moreno, then, said I; rascal that he is, to charge me with abusing persons of honour. A scoundrel, said I, that it is a shame for Death to be seen in his company, and who was never fit for anything in his whole life, but to furnish matter for a farce. That is my grievance, gentlemen, replied Don Diego, for which, with your leave, he shall give me satisfaction. I do not stand upon the matter of being a cuckold, for there is many a brave fellow lives in Cuckold's Row: But why does he not name others as well as me? As if the horn grew upon nobody's head but mine: I am sure there are others that a thousand times better deserve it. I hope he cannot say that ever I gored any of my superiors; or that my being cornuted has raised the price of posthorns, lanthorns, or pocket-inkhorns. Are not shoeing-horns and knife-handles as cheap now as ever? Why must I walk the stage, then, more than my neighbours? I can faithfully say that there never lived a more peaceable wretch upon the face of the earth, all things considered, than myself. Never was man more free from jealousy, or more careful to step aside at the time of a visit; for I hated to spoil sport, when I could make none myself. I confess I was not so charitable to the poor as I might have been; the truth of it is, I watched them as a cat would do a mouse, for I did not love them: But then in requital, I could have out-snorted the seven sleepers, when any of the better sort came to have a private *téte â téte* with my wife. In a word, we agreed blessedly well together, she and I; for I did whatever she thought proper; and she would often say, Long live my poor Diego, the best conditioned, the most complaisant husband in the world: whatever I do is well done, and he never so much as finds fault with it. But, by her leave, that was little to my credit; and the jade, when she said it, was beside the point; for many a time have I said, this is well, and that is ill. When there came any poets to our house, fiddlers, or morris-dancers, I would say, This is not well: But when rich merchants came, Oh! very good, would I say, this is as well as can be. Sometimes we had the luck to be visited by some pennyless courtier, or lowly country officer, then would I take her aside and rattle her to some purpose: Sweetheart, would I say, pray what have we to do with these frippery fellows? Shake them off, I would advise you, and take this for a warning; But when any came that had to do with the mint or exchequer, and spent freely, for lightly come, lightly go, ay marry, my dear, would I say, there is nothing to be lost by keeping such company. And where is the hurt of all this? Nay, on the contrary, my poor wife enjoyed herself happily under the protection of my shadow, so that not an officer durst come near her. Why should this buffoon of a poetaster, then, make me still the ridiculous entertainment of his interludes and farces, and the fool in the play? By your favour, cried I, we are not yet upon even terms; and before we part, you shall know what it is to stir up the resentment of a poet. If thou wert but now alive, I would write thee to death, as Archilocus did Lycambes; And I am determined to put the history of thy life in one of the keenest satires I can write, and call it, The Life and Death of Don Diego Moreno. It shall go hard, cried he, but I will prevent that, and so we fell bloodily to it again, till, at length, the very fancy of a scuffle waked me, and I found myself as weary as if I had been really engaged. I began then to reflect upon the particulars of my dream; and to consider what advantage I might draw from it; for the dead are past jesting, and those are the soundest counsels which we receive from people who can neither be affected by interest nor passion.

III

OF THE LAST JUDGMENT

DREAMS, especially those of sovereigns and princes, are, by Homer, said to proceed from Jove, if the matter of them be pious and important: And it is likewise the judgment of the celebrated Propertius, that good dreams coming from above, have their weight and ought to be credited. And truly I agree with him in the case of a dream I had last night. As I was reading a discourse concerning the end of the world, I fell asleep over the book, and dreamed of the Last Judgment: A thing which, in the house of a poet, is scarce admitted, so much as in a dream. This fancy brought into my mind a passage in Claudian; That all creatures dream at night of what they have heard and seen in the day, as the hound dreams of hunting the hare.

I thought I saw a very beautiful youth towering in the air, and sounding a trumpet; but the forcing of his breath did indeed take much from his beauty. The very marbles, I perceived, and the dead were obedient to his call; for, in the same moment the earth began to open and set the bones at liberty, to seek their fellows. The first that appeared were swordsmen; as generals of armies, captains, lieutenants and common soldiers; who, supposing that it had sounded a charge, sprung from their graves with such briskness and resolution, as if they had been going to an assault, or a combat. The misers peeped out, pale and trembling, for fear of being robbed; the cavaliers and good fellows imagined they had been going to a horse-race, or a hunting-match: And, in a word, though they all heard the trumpet, there was not any creature understood the meaning of it; for I could read their thoughts by their looks and gestures. After this, there appeared several souls, whereof some came up to their bodies, with much difficulty and horror; others stood watching at a distance, not daring to

approach so horrid a spectacle: This wanted an arm, that an eye, and the other
a head. Upon the whole, though I could not but smile at the prospect of so
strange an olio of figures, yet was it not without just matter of admiration at
the All-powerful Providence, to see order drawn out of confusion, and every
part restored to the right owner. I then imagined myself in a churchyard, and
there, methought, several that were unwilling to appear, were changing of
heads; and an attorney would have demurred, upon pretence that he had got
a soul which was none of his own, and that his body and soul were not fellows.

At length, when the whole assembly came to understand that this was the
Day of Judgment, it is worth while to observe what shifting and shuffling there
was among the wicked. The epicure and whoremaster would not own their eyes,
nor the slanderer his tongue; because they would be sure to appear in evidence
against them. The pick-pockets ran away as hard as they could drive from their
own fingers. There was one that had been embalmed in Egypt; and staying for
his guts, an old usurer asked him if the bags were to rise with the bodies? I
could have laughed at this question, but I was presently taken up with a crowd
of cutpurses, running full speed from their own ears, that were offered them
again, for fear of the sad stories they expected to hear. I saw all this from a
convenient standing; and in the instant, there was an outcry at my feet, of
Withdraw, Withdraw. As soon as I heard this, down I came, and immediately
a great many beautiful ladies put forth their heads, and called me clown, for
not paying them that respect and ceremony which is due to their quality. You
must know that the women stand upon punctilios, even in hell itself. They
seemed at first very gay and frolicsome; and well enough pleased to be seen
naked, for they were clean skinned, and well made. But when they came to
understand that this was the Great Day of Account their consciences took check,
and all their jollity was dashed in a moment: Whereupon they retired to a valley,
very much out of humour. There was one among the rest that had had seven husbands, and promised every one of them never to marry again, for she was certain
she could never love anybody else: This lady was casting about for excuses,
and what answer she should make to that point. Another that had been as common as Ratcliff Highway, would neither lead nor drive; and stood humming and
hawing a good while, pretending she had forgotten her night-clothes, and such
fooleries; but, notwithstanding all her excuses, she was brought at last within
sight of the throne; where she found all her old acquaintance, that she had
carried part of their way to hell; who no sooner beheld her, but they fell to
pointing or hooting, so that she took to her heels, and herded herself in a troop

of serjeants. After this I saw several people driving a physician along the bank of the river; and these were only such as he had unnecessarily despatched before their time. They followed him with the cries of Justice, Justice, and forced him on toward the Judgment Seat, where they arrived, in the end, with much ado. While this passed, I heard, methought, on my left hand, a paddling in the water, as if one had been swimming: And what should this be, but a judge, in the midst of a river, washing his hands. I asked him the meaning of it; and he told me, that in his lifetime he had been often daubed in the fist, to make the business slip the better; and he would willingly get out the grease before he came to hold up his hand at the bar. There followed next a multitude of vintners and tailors, under the guard of a legion of devils, armed with rods, whips, cudgels and other instruments of correction: And these counted themselves deaf, and were very unwilling to leave their graves, for fear of a worse lodging. As they were passing on, up started a little lawyer, and asked whither they were going? They replied, that they were going to give an account of their works. With that the lawyer threw himself flat upon his belly, in his hole again: If I am to go downwards at last, says he, I am thus much onward on my way. The vintner sweated as he walked, till one drop followed another: That is well done, cried a devil at his elbow, to purge out thy water, that we may have none in our wine. There was a tailor wrapped up in sarcenets, crook-fingered and baker-legged, who was quite silent all the way he went, but, Alas! alas! how can any man be a thief that dies for want of bread? But his companions gave him a rebuke for discrediting his trade. The next that appeared were a band of highwaymen, following upon the heels of one another, in great distrust and jealousy of thieves among themselves. These were fetched up by a party of devils, in the turning of a hand, and lodged with the tailors: For, said one of the company, your highwayman is but a wild tailor. They were a little quarrelsome at first, but in the conclusion, they went down into the valley and kennelled quietly together. After these came Folly, with her gang of poets, fiddlers, lovers and fencers; the people of all the world that dream the least of a day of reckoning: These were disposed of among the hangmen, Jews, scribes, and philosophers. There were likewise several solicitors, wondering among themselves that they should have so much conscience when they were dead, and none at all while living.

At length, silence being proclaimed, the throne erected, and the great day come; a day of comfort to the good, and of terror to the wicked: the sun and the stars waited at the footstool; the winds were still; the waters quiet; the earth in suspense and anguish for fear of her children; and, in a word, the whole creation in anxiety and disorder. The righteous were employed in prayers and thanksgivings, and the ungodly in framing shifts and evasions to extenuate their crimes. The guardian angels were near, on the one side, to acquit themselves of their duties and commissions; and, on the other side, were the devils, hunting for more matters of aggravation and charge against offenders. The Ten Commandments had the guard of a narrow gate; which was so straight, that the most mortified body could not pass it without leaving a good part of his skin behind him.

On one hand were multitudes of disgraces, misfortunes, plagues, griefs and troubles, all in a clamour against the physicians. The Plague confessed, indeed, that she had struck many; but it was the doctor did their business. Melancholy and Disgrace said the same; and Misfortunes of all kinds made open protestation, that they never brought any man to his grave, without the assistance and advice of a doctor: so that the gentlemen of the faculty were called to account for those they had killed. They took their places upon a scaffold, with pen, ink, and paper about them; and still, as the dead were called, some or other of them answered to the name, and declared the year and day when such a patient passed through his prescriptions.

They began the inquiry at Adam, who, methought, was severely handled about an apple. Alas! cried Judas, who was by, if that were such a fault, what will become of me, that sold and betrayed my Lord and Master?

Next came the Patriarchs, and then the Apostles, who took their places by St. Peter. It was worth remarking, that at this day there was no distinction between kings and beggars before the Judgment-seat. Herod and Pilate, as soon as they put out their heads, found it was like to go hard with them. My judgment is just, said Pilate. Alack! cried Herod, what have I to trust to? Heaven is no place for me; and in limbo I should fall among the innocents I have murdered; so that, without more ado, I must take up my lodging in hell, the common receptacle of cruel offenders.

There came in immediately upon this a kind of grim looking fellow; who, stretching out his arm, cried out, Here are my letters. The company wondered at his humour, and asked the porter what he was? which he himself overhearing, said, I am a master of the noble science of defence; and plucking out several sealed parchments, these, said he, are the attestations of my achievements. At this, all his testimonials dropped out of his hand, and a couple of devils would fain have taken them up, to have brought them in evidence against him at his trial; but the fencer was too nimble for them, and took them up himself. At which an angel offered to lend him his hand, to help him in; but he, for fear of an attack, leaped a step backward, and, with great agility, making a bow, Now, says he, if you think fit I will give you a taste of my skill. The company fell a laughing, and this sentence was passed upon him: That since, by his rules of art, he had occasioned so many duels and murders, he should himself go to the devil by a perpendicular line. He pleaded for himself, that he was no mathematician, and knew no such line; but while the word was in his mouth, a devil came up to him, turned him round about, and down he tumbled.

After him came the treasurers, and such a cry following them for cheating and stealing, that some said thieves were coming, others said no; and the company was divided upon it. They were much troubled at the word thieves, and desired the benefit of counsel to plead their cause. And very good reason, said one of the devils, here is a discarded apostle that has executed both offices, let them take him; where is Judas? When the treasurers heard that, they turned aside, and, by chance, spied in a devil's hand a huge roll of accusations, ready drawn into a formal charge against them. With that, one of the boldest amongst them cried out, Away with these informations; we will rather come to a fine, and compound, though it were for ten or twenty thousand years in Purgatory. Ha! ha! replied the devil, a cunning snap that drew up the charge, if you are upon these terms, you are hard put to it. Whereupon the treasurers being brought to a forced put, were even glad to make the best of a bad game and follow the fencer.

These were no sooner gone, but in came an unlucky pastry-man, whom they asked if he would be tried. That is, even as it hits, said he. Upon this the devil that managed the cause against him, pressed his charge, and laid it home to him, that he had put off cats for hares, and filled his pies with bones instead of flesh; and not only so, but that he had sold horse-flesh, dogs and foxes for beef and mutton; in short, it was proved against him, that Noah never had so many animals in his ark, as this poor fellow had put into his pies; for we read of no rats and mice there; so that he even gave up his cause, and went away to see if his oven was hot.

After this came the philosophers, with their syllogisms; and it was no ill entertainment to hear them chop logic, and put all their expostulations in mood and figure. But the pleasantest people of all were the poets, who insisted upon it that they were to be tried by Jupiter: and to the charge of worshipping false gods, their answer was, that through them they worshipped the true one,

and were rather mistaken in the name than the worship. Virgil had much to
say for himself for his *Sicelides Musæ;* but Orpheus interrupted him, who, being
the father of the poets, desired to be heard for them all. What he! cried one
of the devils; yes, for teaching that boys were better bedfellows than wenches;
but the women would have combed his coxcomb, if they could have caught him.
Away with him to hell once again, was then the general cry, and let him get
out now if he can. So with him all the poets marched off, he showing the way,
because he had been there once before.

As soon as the poets were gone, there knocked at the gate a rich penurious
chuff; but it was told him that the Ten Commandments kept it, and that he
had not kept them. It is impossible, said he, under favour, to prove that ever
I broke any of them. And so he went to justify himself from point to point : he
had done this and that; and had never done that nor the other; but, in the end,
he was delivered over to be rewarded according to his works. And then advanced
a company of house-breakers and robbers; so dexterous, some of them, that they
saved themselves from the very ladder. The scriveners and attorneys observing
that, ah! thought they, if we could but pass for thieves now! and yet they set
a good face enough upon the business too; which made Judas and Mahomet
hope well of themselves; for, said they, if any of these fellows comes off, there
is no fear of us; whereupon they advanced resolutely, with a resolution to take
their trial, which set the devils all a laughing. The guardian angels of the
scriveners and attorneys moved that the Evangelists might be their counsel, which
the devils opposed; for, said they, we shall insist only upon the matter of
fact, and leave them without any possibility of reply or excuse. We might, indeed,
content ourselves with the bare proof of what they are; for it is crime enough
that they are scriveners and attorneys. With that the scriveners denied their
trade, alleging that they were secretaries; and the attorneys called themselves
solicitors. All was said, in effect, that the case would bear; but the best part of
the plea was their doing their duty. In short, after several replications and
rejoinders, they were all sent to the devil, save only one or two that found
mercy. Well, cried one of the scriveners, thus it is to keep lewd company! The
devils called out then to clear the bar, and said they should have occasion for
the scriveners themselves, to enter protestation, in the quality of public notaries,
against lawless and disorderly people; but the poor wretches, it seems, could not
hear on that ear. To say the truth, the Christians were much more troublesome
than the Pagans, which the Devil took exceeding ill; but they had this to say
for themselves, that they were christened when they were children, so that it

was none of their fault, and their parents must answer for it. Judas and Mahomet took such courage, when they saw two or three of the scriveners and attorneys saved, that they were just upon the point of challenging their clergy; but they were prevented by the doctor I told you of, who was first set to the bar, in company with an apothecary and a barber, when a certain devil, with a great bundle of evidences in his hand, told the court, that the greatest part of the dead there present were sent thither by the doctor then at the bar, in confederacy with the apothecary and barber, to whom they were to acknowledge their obligation. An angel then interposing for the defendant, recommended the apothecary for a charitable person, and one that had physicked the poor for nothing: That signifies nothing, cried the Devil, for I have him in my books, and am able to prove that he has killed more people with two little boxes, than the King of Spain has done with two thousand barrels of powder in the Low Country wars. All his medicines are corrupted, and his compositions hold perfect intelligence with the plague: he has entirely depopulated a couple of his neigh-bouring villages, in a matter of three weeks time. The doctor, he let fly upon the apothecary too, and said, he would maintain, against the whole college, that his own prescriptions were according to the Dispensatory; and, if any apothecary would play the knave or fool, and put in this for that, he was not to blame. So that, without any more words, the apothecary was brought in guilty and the doctor and barber were brought off, at the intercession of St. Cosmus and St. Damian.

A dapper lawyer came next, with his tongue steeped in oil, and a great matter of his words and actions; an excellent flatterer, and no man better skilled in the art of moving the passions than himself or more ready at bolting a lucky precedent, at a dead lift, or at making the best of a bad cause; for he had all the shifts and starting-holes in the law at his fingers ends. But all this would not serve; for the verdict went against him, and he was ordered to pay costs. In that instant, there was a discovery made of a fellow that hid himself in a corner, and looked like a spy: they asked him what he was? he made answer, an empiric: What, said a devil, my old friend Pontæus: alas! alas! thou hadst ten thousand times better be in Covent Garden now, or at Charing Cross; for, upon my word, thou wilt have nothing to do here, unless, perhaps, for an ointment for a burn or so: Pontæus therefore retired.

After him came a company of vintners, who were accused for adulterating and mingling water with their wines. Their plea was, that in compensation, they had furnished the hospitals with communion-wine that was right, upon free cost; but this excuse signified as little as that of the tailors there present, who suggested that they had clothed many friars *gratis;* they were therefore despatched away together.

Then followed a number of bankers that had turned bankrupts, to cheat their creditors; who, finding there several of their old correspondents, that they had reduced to a morsel of bread, began to treat of composition. But one of the devils presently cried out, All the rest have had enough to do to answer for themselves; but these people are to reckon for other men's scores as well as their own. And hereupon they were forthwith sent away to Pluto with letters of exchange; but, as it happened at that time, the devil was out of cash.

After this entered a Spanish cavalier, as upright as Justice itself. He was a full quarter of an hour making bows and reverences to the company. We could see no head he had, for his prodigious starched ruff, that stood staring up like a Turkey-cock's tail, and covered it. In a word, it was so fantastic a figure, that the porter was gaping at it a good while, and asked if it were a man or no? It is a man, cried the Spaniard, upon the honour of a cavalier, and his name is Don Pedro Rhodomontodoso. He was so long telling his name and titles, that one of the devils burst out a-laughing in the middle of his pedigree, and demanded what he would be at? Glory, replied he; which they taking in the worst sense, for pride, immediately despatched him to Lucifer. He was a little severe upon his guides, for disordering his mustachoes; but they helped him presently to a pair of beard-irons, and all was well again.

In the next place came a fellow weeping and lamenting; But my masters, says he, my cause is never the worse for my crying; for, if I would stand upon my merits, I could tell you that I have kept as good company, and had as much to do with the saints, as any other body. What have we here, cried one; Diocletian or Nero; for they had enough to do with the saints, though it were but to persecute them. But upon the upshot, what was the poor creature, but a small officer, that swept the church, and dusted the images and pictures. His charge was for stealing the oil out of the lamps, and leaving all in the dark, pretending that the owls and jackdaws had drank it up. He had a trick too of clothing himself out of the church-habits, which he got dyed another colour; and of thickening his soup with consecrated bread, that he stole every Sunday. What he said for himself, I know not; but he had his mittimus, and took the left hand way at parting.

No sooner was he gone, than a voice was heard, Make way there, clear the passage. This was for a flock of handsome, buxom courtesans, in their caps and feathers, that came dancing, laughing and singing of ballads and lampoons, and as merry as anybody could be. They presently changed their note, however, for as soon as they ever beheld the terrible looks of the devils, they fell into violent fits, beating their breasts, and tearing their hair, with all the horror and fury imaginable. An angel pleaded in their favour, that they had been great frequenters of our Lady's chapel: Yes, yes, cried a devil, less of her chapel and more of her virtue, would have done well. There was a notable whipster among the rest, that confessed the devil had reason; and then her trial came on, for making a cloak of the sacrament; and only marrying that she might play the whore with privilege, and never want a father for her bastards. It was her fortune alone to be condemned; and going along, Well, cried she, if I had imagined it would have come to this, I should never have troubled myself with so many masses.

At last, after long waiting, came Judas and Mahomet upon the stage, and to them Jack of Leyden: up comes an officer, and asked which of the three was Judas? I am he, said Jack of Leyden; Nay, but I am Judas, cried Mahomet. They are a couple of lying rascals, says Judas himself, for I am the man, only the rogues make use of my name to save their credit. It is true, I sold my Master once, and the world has been ever since the better for it; but these villains sell him and themselves too every hour of the day; and there follows nothing but misery and confusion. So they were all three packed away to their disciples.

The angel that kept the book found that the sergeants and remembrancers were to come on next; whereupon they were called, and appeared; but the court was not much troubled with them; for they confessed guilty at the first word and were condemned without more ado.

After them came an astrologer, loaden with almanacks, globes, astrolabes, &c., making proclamation, as loud as he could bawl, that there must be a gross mistake in the reckoning; for Saturn had not finished his course, and the world could not yet be at an end. One of the devils that saw how he came provided, looked upon him as his own already: A provident slave, cried he, I warrant him, to bring his firing along with him. But this I must needs tell you, says he to the mathematician, it is a strange thing you should create so many heavens in your life, and go to the devil for want of one after your death. Nay, for going, cried the astrologer, you shall excuse me; if you will carry me, you are very welcome: and immediately order was given to carry him away, and pay the porter.

As he disappeared, methought the court rose; the throne vanished; the shadows and darkness withdrew; the air sweetened; the earth was covered with flowers; and the heavens were clear. I waked, very well pleased to find that, after all this, I was still in my bed and among the living. The use I made of my dream was this: I betook myself presently to my prayers, firmly resolved to forsake my former ways, and, putting my soul into a frame of piety and obedience, peaceably, and with heart-felt satisfaction, wait the coming of that day, when the Almighty Judge of heaven and earth shall be seated on his throne, to reward everyone according to the deeds done in the body.

IV

OF LOVING FOOLS

EARLY one cold winter's morning, when it was better being in a warm bed with a good bedfellow, than wandering about the streets, as I lay advising with my pillow, tumbling and tossing a thousand love-toys in my head, I passed from one fancy to another, till at last I fell asleep and there appeared to me the genius of Conviction, displaying to me all the follies and vanities of love, and supporting her opinions with great authorities and reasons. I was transported, methought, I know not how, into a beautiful meadow, infinitely superior to the fictions of half-witted poets, with all their far-fetching gilding enamel ; a paper of verses is worth nothing with them, unless they force nature for it, and rifle both the Indies. This delicious field was watered with two rivulets; the one bitter, the other sweet; and yet they mingled their streams with a sweet kind of murmur, equal, perhaps to the best music in the world. Love made use of these waters to temper his darts; for, while I was upon the prospect of the place, I saw several of Cupid's little officers and subjects dipping of arrows there, for their amusement and ease. Upon this, I fancied myself in one of the gardens of Cyprus, and that I saw the very hive where the bee lived that stung my young master, and occasioned that excellent ode which Anacreon has written upon the subject. The next thing I beheld was a palace in the midst of the meadow; a beautiful fabric, as well for structure as design. The porches were of the Doric order, excellently wrought; and the pedestals, bases, columns, cornices, capitals, architraves, friezes, and, in short, the whole front of the fabric was ornamented with imaginary trophies, and triumphs of love, in *bas relievo;* which as they were intermixed with other fantastical conceits, carried the face of several little histories, and greatly beautified the building. Over the porch there was, in golden letters, upon black marble, the following inscription:

This is called Fool's Paradise,
From the loving fools that dwelt in't:
Where fools command the wise,
And all live safe and well in't.

It was admirably well finished; the portal spacious; the doors always open, and the house free to all comers, which were not very few; the porter's place was supplied by a woman, very beautiful, both for face and person; tall, delicately shaped, and set off with the advantages of dress and jewels. In a word she was altogether charming; and her name, as I understood, was Beauty. She would let a man in to see the house for a look; and that was all I paid for my passage. In the first court, I found several of both sexes, but so altered in habit and countenance, that they could scarce know one another. They were sad and pensive, and their complexions tainted with a yellow paleness, which Ovid calls Cupid's livery. There was no talk of being true to friends, loyal to superiors, and dutiful to parents; but kindred did the office of procurers; and procurers were called cousins. Wives loved their husband's she friends; and husbands did as much for them, in loving their gallants.

While I was contemplating these encouragers of affection, there appeared a strange extravagant figure, but in the likeness of a human creature. It was neither perfectly man, nor perfectly woman, but had, indeed, a resemblance of both. This person I perceived was very busy up and down, going and coming, beset all over with eyes and ears, had one of the craftiest distrustful looks I ever beheld; and, as I observed, no small authority in the place, which made me enquire after its name and office.   My name, said she, for now it proved to be a woman, is Jealousy, and methinks you and I should be better acquainted; for how came you here else? However, for your satisfaction you are to understand that the generality of the distempered people you see here are of my collecting; and yet I am not their physician but their tormenter, and serve only to aggravate and embitter their misfortunes. If you would know anything farther of the house, never ask me, for it is forty to one but I tell you a lie; I have not told you half the truth, even of myself and to deal plainly with you, I am made up of invention, artifice, and imposture; but the good old man walks there, who is the master of this abode, will tell you all if you will but bear with his slow way of delivery.

No sooner had she said this, than I went to the reverend gentleman, whom I knew presently to be Time, and desired him to let me look into the several quarters and lodgings of the house, for there were some fools of my acquaintance I would gladly visit. He informed me that he was at present so busy about making caudles, cock-broths and jellies for his patients that he could not stir; but yet he directed me where I might find all those I enquired for, and gave me the freedom of the house to walk where I choosed.

I passed out of the first court, into the maid's quarter, which was the very strongest part of the building; and so it had need, for many of the young wenches were so extravagant and furious, that no other place would have held them. The wives and widows were in another room apart. Here might be observed one sobbing and raging with the jealousy of a rival; there another stark mad for a husband, and inwardly bleeding, because she durst not discover it : A third writing letters, all riddle and mystery, mending and marring, till at last the paper had more blots than words in it; some were practising in the glass the gracious smiles, the roll of the eye, and the velvet lip; others, again, were in a diet of oatmeal, clay, chalk, coal, hard wax, and the like; and some were conditioning with their servants for a ball or serenade that the whole town might ring of their address. Yes, some cried, you can go to the park with this lady, and to a play with that lady, and to Banstead with another lady, and spend whole nights at quadrille with Lady Pen-tweezle; but you are ashamed to be seen in my company. Some I saw upon the very point of sealing and delivering. I am thine, cries one, and thine alone : But be sure you be constant. In one corner might be seen maids praying for husbands, that they might better love at random; in another nothing would please them but to be married men's wives, and this disease was looked upon as a little desperate : Some again stood ready furnished with love-letters and tickets, to be cast out at the window, or thrust under the door; and these were looked upon not only as fools, but beasts.

I had seen as much already as I desired; for I had learned of old that he that keeps such company seldom comes off without a scratched face; but if he misses a mistress, he gets a wife, and stands condemned to a repentance, without redemption, unless one of the two dies. Women, in this case, are worse than pirates; a galley-slave may compound for his freedom, but there is no thought of ransom in case of matrimony. I had a good mind to have a little chat with some of them, but, thought I, they will fancy I am in love with them : and so I even marched off into the married quarter.

Here there was such ranting, damning and tearing, as if hell had been broke loose. This proceeded from several women who had been locked up and shackled by their husbands, to keep them in obedience, and who had now broken their prisons and their chains, and were grown ten times madder than before. Some I saw caressing and coxing their husbands, in the very moment they designed to betray them; others were picking their husbands pockets, to maintain now and then a bye blow. Some again were upon a religious point, and all in the humour of promoting pilgrimages and lectures; when, alas! they had no other business with the altars and churches, than a sacrifice to Venus, or a love-meeting. Many there were that went to the Bath; but bathing was the least part of the errand; others to confession, that mistook their gallant for their confessor. Some, to be revenged of jealous husbands, were resolving to do the thing they feared, and pay them in their own coin; others were for making sure beforehand, by way of advance; for that revenge, they say, is as sweet as muscadine and eggs. One was melancholy for a delay; another for a defeat; and a third preparing to make her market at a play. There was one amongst the rest never out of her coach; and asking her the reason, she told me she loved to be jolted. In this crowd of women, you must know there were no wives of ambassadors, soldiers, or merchants, that were abroad upon commission! for such were considered, in effect, as single women, and not allowed as members of this commonwealth.

The next quarter was that of the grave and wise; the right reverend widows; women, in appearance, of surprising severity and reserve, and yet every one of them with her weak side; and you might read her folly and distemper through her disguise. One of them I saw crying with one eye for the loss of one husband, and leering with the other upon him that was to come next. Another, with the Ephesian matron, was solacing herself with her gallant before her husband was cold in the grave; considering that he died half an hour ago, was as dead as Henry the Eight. There were several passing to and fro, quite out of their mourning that looked as demurely as if butter would not have melted in their mouths ; and yet apostate widows, as I was told, though kept as strictly as if they had been in the inquisition. Some were laying wagers whose mourning was most fashionable and best made; or whose peak or veil became the best, and setting themselves off with a thousand tricks of ornament and dress. The widows, I observed, that were marching off with the mark out of their mouths, were hugely concerned to be thought young, and still talking of masques, balls, drums and treats; chanting and jigging to every tune they heard; and all upon the hoity-toity, like mad wenches of fifteen. The younger, on the other side, made use of their time, and took pleasure while it was to be had. There were two of the religious strain; a people much at their beads, and in private. These were there in the quality of Platonists, and under the penance of perpetual abstinence from the flesh they loved best, which is the most mortifying Lent of all other. Some that had skill in perspective were before the glass with their boxes of paint about them; shadowing, drawing out, refreshing and, in short, covering and palliating all the imperfections of feature and complexion, everyone after her own fancy. Now these women were absolutely insufferable; for they were most of them old and headstrong, having got the better of their husbands, so that they would be taking upon them to domineer here as they had done at home; and, indeed, they found the master of the college enough to do.

After taking a proper view of this variety of folly and madness, I went to the devotees, where I found several women and girls that had cloistered themselves up from the conversation of the world, and yet were as giddy as their fellows. These, one would have thought, might have been easily remedied, but many of them were in for their lives, in despite of either counsel or physic. The room where they were was barricaded with strong bars of iron; and yet, when the fancy took them, they would make now and then a sally: For when the fit was upon them they would own no superior but love, come what would of it in the event. The greater part of these good people were writing tickets and despatches, which had still the sign of the cross at the top, and Satan at the bottom; concluding with this, or some such postscript, I commend this paper to your discretion. The fools of this province were continually prating; and, if it happened that any one of them had talked herself weary, which very seldom happened, she would presently take upon her very gravely to admonish the rest, and read a lecture of silence to the company. There were some that, for want of better entertainment, fell in love with one another; but these were looked upon as a sort of fops, and therefore the more favourably used; but they would have been of another mind if they had known the cause of their distemper.

All these various extravagances proceeded from idleness, which according to Petrarch's observation, never fails to make way for wantonness. There was one among the rest that had more letters of exchange upon the credit of her insatiable desires, than a whole company of bankers. Some of these were sick of their old visitor, and called for a fresh man; others, by intervals, I perceived had their wits about them and contented themselves discreetly with the physician of the house. In short, it even pitied my heart to see so many poor people so much distressed, and without any hope of relief, as I learned from him that had them in care; for they were still fidgetting and rolling their bodies; and, if they got a little ease for the present, they would be down again, as soon as they had taken their medicine.

Next I went to the single women, such as made profession never to marry, which were the least outrageous and discomposed of all; for they had numberless ways to lay the devil as well as to raise him. Some of them lived like common highwaymen, by robbing Peter to pay Paul, and stripping honest men to clothe rascals; which is, under favour, but a lewd kind of charity. Others there were that were absolutely out of their senses, and as mad as March hares, for this wit, and the other poet, that failed to pay them again in rhymes and madrigals, with ruby lips, and pearly teeth; so that to read their verses, one would imagine the whole women to be directly turned into stone.

> *Of sapphire fair, or crystal clear,*
> *Is the forehead of my dear.*

I saw one entreating a cunning old man to tell her her fortune; another dealing with a conjurer for a philtre or drink to make her beloved; a third was daubing and patching up an old ruined face to make it fresh and young again; but she might have as well washed a blackamoor white. In fine, numbers there were that, with their borrowed hair, teeth, eyes and eyebrows, looked like fine folks at a distance; but would have been left as ridiculous as Æsop's crow, if every bird had plucked off his own feather. Deliver me, thought I, smiling and shaking my head, if this be woman.

From these I went to the men's quarter, which was but next door, and only divided by a thick wall. Their great misery was that they were dead to good advice, obstinately hating and despising both physic and physician; for if they would have either quitted or changed, they might have been cured: but they chose rather to die; and, though they saw their error, would not mend it; which brought the following old rhyme into my head:

> *The doctor's a blockhead,*
> *When love's in the head.*

These fools-male were all in the same chamber; and one might perfectly read their humour and distemper in their looks and gestures. Oh! how many a gay lad did I see there, in his point cravat, and embroidered vest, that had not a whole shirt to his back; How many bullies, that had nothing else in their mouths, but the lives and fortunes they would spend in their sweet ladies' service! that would yet have run five miles on your errand, to have been treated but to a threepenny ordinary! How many a poor devil that was just starving, and was yet troubled with the rebellion of the flesh. Some there were that spent much time in setting their perukes, ordering the moustaches, and dressing up the very face of Lucifer himself for a beauty; the woman's privilege, and in truth an encroachment to their prejudice. There were others that made it their glory to pass for Hectors; sons of Priam; brothers of the blade; and talked of nothing but attacks, combats, reverses and stoccadoes; not considering that a naked weapon is present death to a timorous woman. Some were taking the rounds of their ladies lodgings at midnight, and went to bed again as wise as they rose; others fell in love by contagion, and merely conversing with the infected. Some, again, went post from church to chapel, every holiday, to seek for a mistress, and so turned a day of rest into a day of labour. There might be seen others skipping continually from house to house, like the knight upon a chessboard, without ever catching the queen they fought after. Some, like crafty beggars, made their case worse than it was; and others, though it were never so bad, durst not so much as open their mouths. Really I was sorry for the poor mutes, and I wished with all my heart their mistresses had been witches, that they might have known their meaning by their mumping; but they were lost to all counsel, so that there was no advising them. There was another species of elevated and conceited lovers. These, it seems, were not to be satisfied without the seven liberal sciences, and the four cardinal virtues, in the shape of a woman; but their case was desperate. The next I saw were a generation of modest fools, that passed under the notion of people diffident of themselves. They were generally men of good understanding but, for the most part, younger brothers of low fortunes, and such as, for want of money to go to the price of higher amours, were obliged teo take up with ordinary stuff, that brought them nothing in the end but beggary and repentance. The husbands, I perceived, were horribly furious, although in manacles and shackles. Some of them left their own wives, and fell upon their neighbours: others, to keep the good woman in awe and obedience, would bluster and play the tyrant; but upon the upshot found their mistake; for, though they came on as fierce as lions, they went off as tame as lambs. Some were making friendships with their wife's she-cousins, and agreeing upon a cross-gossipping, whoever should have the first child.

The widowers that had a bit of the bridle passed from place to place, where they stayed more or less, according to their entertainment and so were in effect as good as married for as long or as short as they themselves thought proper.

E

These lived single, and spent their time in visiting, first one friend, then another. Here they fell in love, there they kindled a jealousy; they themselves were jealous in one place, and cured in another: but the miracle was that they all knew, and confessed themselves a company of fools, and yet continued so. Those that had skill in music, and could either sing or play, made use of their gifts, to put the silly wenches that were but half-moped before, directly out of their wits. They that were poetical were continually hammering upon the subjects of cruelty and disappointment. One tells his good fortune to another, that requites him with the story of his bad luck. They that had set their hearts upon girls were beating the streets all day, to find the avenues to a lady's lodgings at night. Some were tampering and caressing the chambermaid, as the easiest way to obtain the mistress; others chose to put it to the push, and attempt the lady herself. Some were examining their pockets, and viewing their furniture; which consisted much in love-letters, delicately sealed up with perfumed wax, upon raw silk; and numberless pretty devices within, all wrapped up in riddle and cypher, together with abundance of hair bracelets, lockets, knots of ribband, and the like. There were others that were called the husband's friends, who were ready upon every occasion to do this and that kindness for the husband. Their purse, credit, coach and horses were all at his service; and, in the meantime, who but they to gallant the wife to the park, the garden, a treat, or a comedy; and to bear them company—forty to one, but they stumble upon an aunt, an old housekeeper of the family, or some such reverend go-between, that is a well-wisher to the mathematics; she takes the hint, performs the good office, and the work is done.

Now there were two sorts of fools for the widows; the one was beloved, and the other not: the latter were content to be a kind of voluntary slaves, for the compassing their ends: but the other were the happier for they were at perfect liberty to do what they thought proper, unless some friend or child of the house perchance came in, in the mischievous nick; and then, in case of a little colour more than ordinary, or a tumbled handkerchief, it was but turning the scene, and struggling for a paper of verses, or some such business, to keep all in countenance. Some made their assaults both with love and money, and they seldom failed, for they came doubly armed and your Spanish pistoles are an irresistible kind of battery.

I came now to reflect upon everything I had beheld; and, as I was walking in that meditation toward another lodging, I found myself, before I was aware, in the first court again where I entered; and in it I observed new wonders: I saw that the number of fools increased every moment; although Time, I perceived, did everything in his power to recover them. There was Jealousy tormenting even those that were most confident of the faith of what they loved. There was Memory rubbing off old scores. There was Understanding locked up in a dark cellar and Reason with both her eyes out. I stopped a little, the better to observe these varieties; and when I had looked till I was tired, I turned about and spied a door, but so narrow, that it was almost impossible to go through it; yea, strait as it was, many there were that Ingratitude and Infidelity had set at liberty and who made a shift to get through. Upon this opportunity of returning, I made as much haste as possible to be one of the first at the door, and in that instant my man drew my curtains, and informed me breakfast waited me. I waked, and recollecting himself, found it was nothing but a dream. The very fancy, however, of having spent so much time in the company of fools and madmen, troubled me a little; but with this comfort that I had found Passionate Love to be nothing but folly, as well when asleep as when waking.

V

OF THE WORLD

How greatly are we deceived in the quality and value of the things we covet, since it is quite impossible for anything in this world to fix our appetites and desires, which are still wavering and changing like pilgrims, delighted with, and nourished by variety! What we pursue with the greatest delight and passion imaginable, yields us nothing but satiety and repentance in the possession : yet, such is the power of these appetites of ours, that, when they call and command, we follow and obey; though we find in the end that what we took for a beauty in the pursuit, proves but a carcase in the quarry, and we are sick of it as soon as we have it. Now the world, that knows our palate and inclination, never fails to feed the humour, and to flatter and entertain us with every kind of change and novelty, as the most certain means of gaining upon our affections.

Such reflections as these, one would imagine, might have put sober thoughts and resolutions into my head; but it was my fate to be taken off in the very middle of my moral speculation, and carried away from myself, by vanity and weakness, into the wide world, where I was soon not much unsatisfied with my condition. As I passed from one place to another, several that saw me, I observed, did but make sport with me; for the farther I went, the more I was at a loss in a labyrinth of delusions. One while, I was in with the swordmen and bravoes; up to the ears in challenges and quarrels, and never without my arm in a scarf, or a broken head : another time I was never well but at some celebrated tavern feasting sumptuously : besides twenty other entertainments, that I found every jot as extravagant as these; which, to my great trouble and admiration, left me not so much as one moment's repose.

As I was in one of my unquiet and pensive moods, somebody called after me, and plucked me by the cloak; which proved to be a person of a venerable age, his clothes very poor and tattered, and his face as if it had been trampled upon in the streets; notwithstanding which he had still the air and appearance of one that deserved much honour and respect. Good Father, said I to him, why should you envy me my enjoyments? Pray let me alone, and do not trouble yourself with me or my doings. You are past the pleasure of life yourself, and cannot endure to see other people merry that have the world before them. Consider of it; you are now upon the point of leaving the world, and I am but newly come into it. But it is the trick of all old men to be carping at the actions of their juniors. Son, said the old man, smiling, I shall neither hinder nor envy thy delights, but in pure pity I would fain reclaim thee. Dost thou know the price of a day, an hour, or a minute? Didst thou ever examine the value of time? If thou hadst, thou wouldst employ it better, and not spend so many blessed opportunities upon trifles, and so easily and insensibly part with so inestimable a treasure. What is become of thy past hours? Have they made thee a promise to come again when thou callest for them? or canst thou show me which way they went? No, no; they are gone without recovery; and in their flight, methinks, Time seems to turn his head, and laugh over his shoulder in derision at those that made no better use of him when they had him. Dost thou know, that all the minutes of our life are but as so many links of a chain that has death at the extremity; and every moment brings thee nearer thy expected solution? Perchance, while the word is speaking, it may be at thy very door: doubtless, at thy rate of living, it will be upon thee before thou art sensible of it. How stupid is he who dies while he lives, for fear of dying! How wicked is he that lives as if he should never die, and only fears death when he comes to feel it! He is certainly none of the wisest that spends all his days in lewdness and debauchery, without considering that, of his whole life, any minute might have been his last.

My good Father, said I, I am very much obliged to you for your excellent discourses, for they have delivered me out of the power of numberless frivolous and vain affections, that had taken possession of me. But who are you, I pray? and what is your business here? My poverty, and these rags, replied he, are enough to tell you that I am an honest man; a friend to truth, and one that will not flatter, when he may speak it to the purpose. Some call me the Plain-Dealer; others, the Undeceiver-General. You see me all in tatters, wounds, scars and bruises. And what is all this but the requital the world gives me for my good counsel and kind visits. Yet, after all this endeavour to drive me from them, they call themselves my friends, though they curse me as soon as ever I come near them, and had rather be hanged than spend one quarter of an hour in my company. If thou hast a mind to see the world I talk of, follow me, and I will carry thee into a place where thou shalt have a full prospect of it; and without any inconvenience, shall see all that is in it, or the people that dwell in it, and look it through and through. What do you call this place? cried I. The Hypocrites' Walk, said he, which crosses the world from one pole to the other. It is extensive and populous; for I believe there is not any man alive but has either a house or a chamber in it. Some live in it altogether; others take it only in passage, for there are hypocrites of all sorts; but all mortals have, more or less, a love for its pleasures. That fellow there in the corner, came but the other day from the plough-tail, and would now fain be a gentleman; but had not he better pay his debts and walk alone, than break his promises to keep a footman? There is another rascal that would fain be a lord, and would venture a voyage to Venice for the title, but that he is better at building castles in the air than upon the water. In the meantime, he puts on a nobleman's face and garb; he swears and drinks like a lord, and keeps his hounds and whores, which it is feared, in the end, will devour their master. Mark now that piece of gravity and form; he walks, you see, as if he moved by clock-work; his words are few and low; he makes all his answers by a shrug or a nod. This is the hypocrite of a minister of state, who, with all his counterfeit of wisdom, is one of the greatest blockheads that ever existed.

Turn about now, and mind those decrepid sots there, that can scarce lift a leg over a threshold, and yet must be dyeing their hair, colouring their beards, and playing over the follies of youth again, with a thousand hobby-horse tricks and antic dresses. On the other side, you have a company of silly boys taking upon them to rule the world under a vizor of wisdom and experience. What lord is that, said I, so magnificently dressed? That lord, said he, is a tailor, in his holiday-clothes and if he were upon his shop-board, his own scissors and needles would hardly know him. You must understand that hypocrisy is so epidemical a disease, that it has laid hold of the trades themselves, as well as the masters. The cobbler must be saluted, Mr. Translator; the groom names himself gentleman of the horse; the fellow that carries guts to the bears, writes, one of his majesty's officers. The hangman calls himself a minister of justice; the mountebank, an able man; and a common whore passes for a courtesan. The bawd acts the Puritan; gaming-ordinaries are called academies, and bawdy-houses places of entertainment. The page styles himself the child of honour; and the lackey calls himself my lady's page; and every pickthank names himself a courtier. The cuckold-maker passes for a fine gentleman; and the cuckold himself for the best-natured husband in the world; and a very ass commences a master-doctor. Hocuspocus tricks are called sleight of hand; lust, friendship; usury, thrift; cheating is but gallantry; lying wears the name of invention; cowardice, weakness of nature; and rashness carries the countenance of valour. In a word, this is all hypocrisy and knavery in disguise; everything is miscalled. Now there are, besides these, certain general applications taken up, which by long usage are almost grown into prescription. Every little whore takes upon her to be a great lady; every gownman to be a counsellor; every bully to be a soldier; every gay thing a cavalier; every parish-clerk a doctor; and every writing-clerk in the office must be called Mr. Secretary. So that the whole world, take it where you will, is but a mere juggle; and you will find that wrath, gluttony, pride, avarice, luxury, murder and numberless other heinous sins, have all of them hypocrisy for their source, and thither will return again. It would be well, said I, if you could prove what you say; but I can hardly see how so great a diversity of waters should proceed from one and the same fountain. I am not surprised, replied he, at your distrust; for you are mistaken, in very good company, to fancy contrariety in many things, which are, in effect, so much alike. It is agreed upon, both by philosophers and divines, that all sins are evil; and you must allow that the will embraces or pursues no evil, but under the resemblance of good; nor does the sin lie in the representation of knowledge of what is evil, but in the consent to it; which consent itself is sinful, although without any subsequent act. It is true, the execution serves afterwards for an aggravation, and ought to be considered under many differences and distinctions; but in short, evident it is that the will entertains no ill, but under the shape of some good. What do you think now of the hypocrite that cuts your throat in his arms, and murders you under pretence of kindness? What is the hope of an hypocrite? says Job. He neither has, nor can have any; for he is wicked as he is an hypocrite; and even his best actions are worth nothing, because they are not what they seem to be; so that of all sinners he has the most to answer for. Other offenders sin only against God; but the hypocrite sins with him, as well as against him, making use of his holy name as a cloak and countenance for his wickedness. For which reason our blessed Redeemer, after many affirmative precepts delivered to his disciples for their instruction, gave only this negative, "Be not sad as the hypocrites", which lays them open in few words; and he might as well have said, Be not hypocrites, and ye shall not be wicked.

We were now come to the place the old man told me of; where I found everything according to my expectation, and took the higher ground, that I might have the better prospect of what passed. The first remarkable thing I beheld was a long funeral train of kindred and guests, following the corpse of a deceased lady, in company with the disconsolate widower, who marched with his chin upon his breast, at a sad and heavy pace; muffled up in a mourning cloak, with at least ten yards of cloth upon his body, and no less in his train. Alas! cried I, that ever I should live to see so sad a spectacle! Oh, blessed woman! how did thy husband love thee in thy lifetime, that follows thee with this infinite faith and affection even to thy grave! And happy the husband, doubtless, in a wife worthy of this kindness! and in so many tender friends and relations, to take part with him in his sorrows. My good father, let me entreat you to observe this doleful encounter. With that, shaking his head and smiling, My son, says he, thou shalt presently see that all this is nothing in the world but vanity, imposture, and constraint; and I will show thee the difference between things themselves and their appearances. To see this vast number of torches, with the magnificence of the ceremony and attendance, one would imagine there should be some mighty matter in the business; but let me assure thee, that this parade comes to no more than Much ado about Nothing. The woman was nothing effectually, even while she lived; the body now in the coffin is somewhat less than nothing; and the funeral honours which are now paid to her, come to just nothing too. But the dead, it seems, must have their vanities, and their holidays, as well as the living. Alas! what is a carcase but the most odious sort of putrefaction? a corrupted earth fit neither for fruit nor tillage. And then for the melancholy countenances of the mourners; they are only troubled at the invitation, and would not care a pin if the inviter and body too were both at the devil. All this you might see by their behaviour and discourses; for when they should have been praying for the dead, they were prating of her pedigree, and her last will and testament. I am not so near akin, says one, but I might have been spared, and I had twenty other things to do; another should have met at a tavern; a third at a play; a fourth mutters that he is not placed according to his quality; another cries out, A pox on your meetings, where there is nothing stirring but worms' meat. Let me tell you farther, that the widower himself is not so sorry as you think for the dead wife, but for the devilish expense in blacks and escutcheons, tapers and mourners; and that she was not fairly laid to rest without all this ado; for he persuades himself that she might have found her way to her grave without a candle. And since she was to die, it is his opinion, that she should have made quicker work of it : for a good wife is like a good Christian, to put her conscience in order betimes, and get her gone, without lingering in the hands of doctors, apothecaries and surgeons, which must murder her husband too : or, to save charges, she might have had the discretion to have died of the plague, which would have prevented company. This is the second wife he has already turned over; and, to give the man his due, he has had the wit to secure himself a third, while this was lying on her death-bed. So that his case is no more than changing a cold wife for a warm one; and he will soon recover this affliction.

The good man, methought, spoke wonders; and being thoroughly convinced of the danger of trusting to appearances, I took up a resolution never to conclude upon anything, though never so plausible, without thoroughly enquiring into it. With that the funeral disappeared, leaving us behind; and, for a farewell, this sentence : I am gone before, you are, in the meantime, to accompany others to their graves, as you have done me; and as I, when time was, have attended others, with as little care and devotion as yourselves.

We were taken off from this meditation by a noise we heard in the house behind us; where we had no sooner set foot over the threshold, but we were entertained with a concert of six voices, that were set and tuned to the sighs and groans of a woman newly become a widow. The passion was acted to the life; but the dead was little the better for it. Sometimes they were seen clapping and wringing their hands; at others, groaning and sighing as if their hearts would break. The hangings, pictures and furniture were all taken down and removed, the rooms hung with black, and in one of them lay the poor disconsolate upon a couch, with her condoling friends about her. It was quite dark, to correspond with the parts they had to play; for there was thus no discovering the horrid faces and strains they made, to fetch up their artificial tears and lamentations. Madam, said one, tears are but thrown away; and really the grief to see your ladyship in this condition has made me as lost to all thought of comfort as yourself. I beseech you, Madam, cheer up, cried another, with almost as many sighs as words, your husband is happy that he is out of this miserable world. He was a good man, and now he finds the sweets of it. Patience, dear Madam, cries a third, it is the will of Heaven, and there is no contending. Dost thou talk of patience, interrupted she, and no contending? Wretched creature that I am ! to outlive that dear man ! Oh that dear husband of mine ! Oh that I should ever live to see this day ! And then she fell to blubbering, sobbing and raving far worse tha nbefore. Alas ! alas ! who will trouble himself with a poor widow now; I have never a friend left to look after me : what shall become of me now?

As soon as she had done, there came in the chorus, with their nose-instruments. There was such blowing, sobbing and snivelling, that there was no enduring the house; and all this, you must know, served them to a double purpose; that is to say, for physic and compliment; for it passed for condolence and purged their heads of ill humours both at once. I could not avoid being sorry for the poor widow; a creature forsaken of all the world and I told my guide as much, and that a charity, as I thought, would be well bestowed upon her. The Scriptures call them Mutes, according to the import of the Hebrew, in regard that they have no body to speak for them. And if at any time they take heart to speak for themselves, they had just as well hold their tongues, for no body minds them. Is there anything more frequently given in charge throughout the whole Bible, than to protect the fatherless and defend the cause of the widow? as the highest and most necessary point of Christian charity, as having neither power nor right to defend themselves. Does not Job, in the depth of his misery and disgraces, make choice to clear himself toward the widow, in his expostulations with the Almighty? "If I have caused the eyes of the widow to fail"; or, "consumed the eyes of the widow", after the Hebrew. So that it seems to me, beside the general duty of charity, that we are also bound by the laws of honour and generosity, to do all in our power to help them; for the poor souls are forced to plead with their eyes, for want of either hands or tongues to assist them. Indeed you must pardon me, my good father, said I, if I cannot hold any longer from bearing a part in this mournful concert, upon this melancholy occasion. And is this, cried the old man, the fruit of your boasted divinity; to sink into weakness and tears, when you have the greatest need of your resolution and prudence? Stop a little, and I will unfold this mystery; though, let me tell you, it is one of the hardest things in nature to make any man as wise as he should be, who imagines himself wise enough already. If this accident of the widow had not happened, we had none of the fine things that have been started upon it: for it is occasion that awakens both our virtue and philosophy; and it is not enough to know the mine where the treasure lies, unless a man has the skill of drawing it out, and making the best of what he has in his possession. What are you the better for all the advantages of wit and learning, unless you have the faculty of reducing what you know into apt and proper application?

Be attentive, and I will show you that this widow, who looks as if she had nothing in her mouth but the service of the dead, and only hallelujahs in her soul; that this mortified piece of formality has green thoughts under her black veil, and brisk imaginations about her, in spite of her calamity and misfortune.

The chamber you see is dark, and the attendants faces are muffled up in funeral
dresses. And what of all this, when the whole course of their mourning is but
a thorough cheat? Their weeping signifies nothing more than crying at so much
an hour; for their tears are hackneyed out; and when they have wept out their
stage, they take up and are quiet. If you would relieve them, leave them to themselves; and as soon as your back is turned you shall find them singing and
dancing, and as merry as crickets. Take away the spectators, their hypocrisy
is at an end, and the play is done; but now the confidants game begins: Come,
come, Madam, faith we must be merry, cries one; we are to live by the living,
and not by the dead. It becomes not a handsome young widow to lie whimpering
away your opportunity, and lose so many excellent matches: there is you know
who, I dare swear, is very much in love with you: by my troth, I wish you
were in bed together, and I would be hanged if you did not find one warm bed-
fellow worth twenty cold ones. Really, Madam, cries a second, she gives you
good counsel, and if I were in your place I would follow it and make use of my
time. It is but one lost, and ten found. Pray tell me, Madam, if I may be so
bold, what is your opinion of that cavalier who was here yesterday? Certainly he
has a great deal of wit; and methinks he is a very genteel smart gentleman. Well,
if that man has not a strange passion for somebody, I will never believe my eyes
again; and, in good faith, if all parties were agreed, I would you were even well
in his arms the night before tomorrow. Were it not a great shame to let such a
beauty lie fallow? This sets the widow simpering; and at length she makes up
her pretty little mouth. It is somewhat of the soonest to talk of these affairs; but
Heaven's will be done. However, Madam, I am obliged to you for your friendly
advice. You have here the very bottom of her sorrow: she has taken a second
husband into her heart, before her first was buried. I should have told you, that
your right widow eats and drinks more the first day of her widowhood than in
any other of her whole life; for there appears not a visitant, but presently out
comes the groaning cake, cold baked meat, or some restorative morsel or other
to comfort the affliction; and the cordial bottle must not be forgotten neither,
for sorrow is dry. So to it they fall, and at every bit the new widow fetches
up a heavy sigh, pretends to chew false and make protestation, that for her part
she can taste nothing; she has quite lost her digestion and has such an oppression
at her stomach, that she dares not eat any more for fear of overcharging nature.
And in truth, says she, how can it be otherwise, since, unhappy creature that I
am! he is gone that gave the relish to all my enjoyments! But there is no recal-
ling him from the grave, and so no remedy but patience. By this time you see,

cried the old man, whether your exclamations were reasonable or not.

She had hardly done speaking, when, hearing an uproar in the crowd, we looked out to see what was the matter; and there we saw a catchpole, without either hat or cravat, out of breath, and his face all bloody, crying out, Help, help, in the king's name; stop thief, stop thief; and all the while running as hard as he could drive after a thief that made away from him, as if the devil had been at his heels. After him came an attorney, all dirty, a vast quantity of papers in his hand, an inkhorn at his girdle, and several nasty people about him; and down he sat himself just before us, to write somewhat upon his knee. Bless me, thought I, how a cause prospers in the hand of one of those fellows; for he had filled his paper in a trice. These catchpoles, said I, had need to be well paid for the hazards they run to secure us in our lives and fortunes; and indeed they deserve it. Look how the poor unfortunate wretch is torn, bruised, and battered, and all this for the good and benefit of the public. Not so fast, cried the old man; I think thou wouldst never leave talking, if I did not stop thy mouth sometimes. You must know that he that made the escape, and the catch-pole, are a couple of ancient friends and pot-companions. Now the catchpole with the thief, for not giving him a fair share in the last booty, and the thief, after a great struggle, and a good many blows, has made a shift to save himself. You will say the rogue had need of good heels to outrun this gallows beagle; for there is hardly any beast can outstrip a bailiff in pursuit. So there is not the least thought of public good in the catchpole's action, but merely a prosecution of his own profit, and a spite to see himself choused. Now if the catchpole, I confess, without any private interest had made this attempt upon the thief, being his friend, to bring him to justice, it had been well; yet, still consider, that it is as natural to let slip a serjeant at a pick-pocket, as a greyhound at a hare. The whip, the pillory, the axe, and the halter, make up the best part of the catch-pole's revenue. These people are of all sorts the most odious in the world; and if men in revenge would resolve to be virtuous, though but for a year or two, they might starve them all. It is, in fine, an unlucky employment; and catch-poles, like devils, have the wages of tormentors.

I hope, said I to my guide, that the attorneys shall have your good word too. Yes, yes, you need not doubt of it, said the old man, for your attorneys and your catchpoles always act in concert. The attorney draws the information, and has all his forms ready, so that it is no more but to fill up the blanks, and away to the gaol with the delinquent: if there be anything to be gotten, it is not a half-penny matter whether the party be guilty or innocent: give but an attorney pen, ink and paper, and let him alone for witnesses. In case of an examination, he has the grace not to insist too much upon plain and naked truth, but to set down only what makes for his purpose, and then, when they come to signing, to read over in the deponent's sense, for his memory is good, what he has written in his own : and by this means, the cause goes on as he pleases. To prevent this villainy, it were well if the examiners were as well sworn to write the truth, as the witnesses are to speak it; and yet there are some honest men of all sorts but among the attorneys : the very calling does by the honest attorneys as the sea does by the dead; it may entertain them for a while, but it presently casts them up again.

My good old friend would have proceeded, if he had not been taken off by the rattling of a gilt coach, and courtier in it, that was blown up as big as pride and vanity could make him. He sat stiff and upright, as if he had swallowed a stake, and made it his glory to show himself in that posture : it would have hurt his eyes to have exchanged a glance with anything that was vulgar, and therefore he was not too profuse of his looks. He had a deep laced ruff on, that was right Spanish, which he wore erect, and so stiff starched, that a man would have thought he had carried his head in a paper lanthorn. He was a great studier of set faces, and much affected with looking politic and big; but for his arms and body he had entirely lost or forgotten the use of them : he could neither bow nor move his hat to any man that saluted him; nor so much as turn from one side to the other, but sat as if he had been boxed up like a Bartholomew baby. After this magnificent statue followed a swarm of gaudy footmen, while his lordship's company in the coach were a buffoon and a para- site. O blessed prince ! said I, to live at this rate in ease and splendour, and to have the world at will? What a glorious train is this! Undoubtedly there never was a great fortune better bestowed. With that the old man took me up, and told me, that the judgment I had made upon this occasion was all dotage and mistake, except only when I said he had the world at will. In that, said he, you have reason; for what is the world but labour, vanity and folly; which is likewise the composition and entertainment of this gentleman?

As for his attendants, let them be examined, and my life for your's you shall find more creditors among them than servants : there are bankers, jewellers, scriveners, brokers, mercers, drapers, tailors, vintners; and are properly the stays, the supporters of this animated machine. His money, meat, drink, robes, liveries, wages, all come out of their pockets; they have his honour for their security, and must content themselves with promises and fair words for full satisfaction, unless they choose a footman with a cudgel for their paymaster. After all this, if this gallant were examined, or a man could enter into the secrets of his conscience, I dare swear it would appear, that he that digs the mine for his bread, lives ten thousand times more at ease than he; with beating of his brains night and day for new shifts, tricks and projects to support his character.

Now, view his companions, his fool and his flatterer. They are too hard for him you see, and eat, drink and make merry at his expense. What greater misery or shame in the world, than for a man to make a friendship with such rascals, and to spend his time and estate in so brutal and insipid a society! it costs him more, besides his credit, to maintain that couple of coxcombs, than would have brought him the conversation of a dozen grave and learned philosophers. But will you now see the bottom of this scandalous and dishonourable kindness: my lord, says the buffoon, you were most infallibly wrapped up in your mother's smock: for let me be hanged if you have not set all the ladies about our court agog. The very truth is, cries the parasite, all the rest of the nobility look like corn-cutters to you; and indeed, wherever you come, you have still the eyes of the whole company upon you. Go, go, gentlemen, says my lord, you must not flatter your friends. This is your kindness, not my desert, and I have an obligation to you for your generosity. After this manner, these asses scrub and curry one another, and play the fool by turns.

Just as the old man was speaking, there passed by us a lady of pleasure, of so excellent shape and garb, that it was impossible to see her without passion for her, and no less impossible to look upon anything else as long as she was in sight: but they that had seen her once were to see her no more; for she turned her face still to newcomers. Her motion was graceful and free; one while she stared you full in the face, under pretence of opening her hood, to set it in better order: by and by she stole a look at you with one eye, and a side-face from the corner of her vizor; like a witch afraid to be known when she comes from a caterwaul; and then out came the delicate hand, and discovered the most delicious neck and breast. Her hair was more artificially disposed into careless rings, and the best red and white in nature was in her cheeks, if that of her lips and teeth did not exceed it. In short, all she looked upon were her own; and this was the vision that pleased me above all the rest. As she was marching off, I could not choose but take up a resolution to follow her; but my old man laid a block in the way, and stopped me at the very starting, which was an affront to a man that was both in love and in haste, that might very well stir his resentment. My officious friend, said I, he that does not love a woman sucked a sow;

and, questionless, he must be either blind or barbarous, that is proof against the charms of so divine a beauty: nor would any but a sot let slip the blessed opportunity of so fair an encounter. A handsome woman! Why, what was she made for, but to be loved? and he that has her has all that is lovely or desirable in nature. For my own part, I would renounce the world for such an one as her, and never desire anything either beyond her or beside her. What lightning does she carry in her eyes! What charms and chains in her looks and motions, for the very souls of her beholders! Was ever anything so clear as her forehead? or so black as her eyebrows? One would swear that her complexion had taken a tincture of vermilion and milk; and that nature had brought her into the world with pearls and rubies in her mouth. In a word, she is the masterpiece of the creation, worthy of infinite praise, and equal to our largest desires and imaginations.

Here the old man interrupted me, and bade me make an end of my discourse; for thou art, said he, a man of much wonder, small experience, and delivered over to the spirit of folly and blindness: thou hast eyes in thy head, and yet not brains enough to know either why they were given thee, or how to use them. Understand then that the office of the eye is to see, but it is the privilege of the soul to distinguish and choose; whereas you either do the contrary, or else nothing, which is worse. He that trusts his eyes exposes his mind to numberless torments and confusions: he shall take clouds for mountains, straight for crooked, one colour for another, or an indisposed medium for a reality. We are not able sometimes to say which way a river runs, till we throw in a twig or straw to discover the current. And what will you say now if this beautiful lady, your new mistress, proves as gross a cheat and impostor as any of the rest? She went to bed last night as ugly as a witch, and yet this morning she comes forth in your opinion a perfect angel. The truth is, she hires all her beauty by the day and if you did but see this puppet taken to pieces, you would find her little else but paint and plaster. To begin her anatomy at the head: you must know that the hair she wears is borrowed of a tire-woman, for her own was blown off by an unlucky wind from the coast of Naples: or, if she has any left, she keeps it private, as a memorial of her antiquity. She is beholden to the pencil for her eyebrows and complexion; and upon the whole is but an old picture refreshed. But the wonder is, to see a picture with life and motion; unless, perhaps, she has got the necromancer's receipt, that made himself young again in his glass bottle: for all that you see of her that is good, comes from distilled waters, essences, powders and the like: and to see the washing of her face would fright the very devil. She abounds in pomatums, sweet waters, Spanish pockets, perfumed drawers; and all little enough to qualify the poisonous whiffs she sends from her toes and arm-pits, which would otherwise out-stink ten thousand pole-cats. She cannot choose but kiss well, for her lips are always bathed in oil and grease; and he that embraces her shall find the better half of her the tailor's and only a stuffing of cotton and canvass to supply the defects of her body. When she goes to bed she puts off one half of her person with her shoes. What do you think of her adored beauty now? or have your eyes deceived you? Well, well, confess your error and mend it: and know that without more descant upon this woman, it is the design and glory of most of the sex to lead silly men captive: nay, take the best of them, and what with the trouble of getting them, and the difficulty of pleasing them, he that comes off best will find himself no great gainer at the bottom of the account. I could recommend you here to other remedies of love, inseparable from the very sex, but I hope I need tell you no more, as you have heard enough already.

F

VI

OF HELL

ONE pleasant night in autumn, when the moon shone very bright, being at a friend's house in the country, which was most delightfully situated, I took a walk into the park, where all my past visions came fresh into my head again, and I was well enough pleased with the meditation. At length the humour took me to leave the path, and go farther into the wood. What impulse carried me to this I cannot tell; whether I was moved by my good angel, or some higher power; but so it was, that in a few minutes I found myself a great distance from home, and in a place where it was no longer night, with the pleasantest prospect round about me that I ever beheld. The air was mild and temperate; and it was no small advantage to the beauty of the place, that it was both serene and silent.

On the one hand, I was entertained with the murmurs of crystal streams; on the other, with the whispering of the trees: the birds singing all the while, either in emulation or requital of the other harmonies. And now, to show the instability of our affections and desires, I was grown weary even of tranquillity itself, and in this most agreeable solitude began to wish for company.

Methought, at that very instant, I perceived two paths issuing from one and the same beginning, but dividing themselves forwards, more and more by degrees, as if they liked not one another's company. That on the right hand was narrow almost beyond imagination; and, being very little frequented, was so overgrown with thorns and brambles, and so stony, that it was almost impossible to get into it. One might see, however, the prints and marks of several passengers that had rubbed through, though with exceeding difficulty; for they had left pieces of heads, arms, legs, feet, and many of them their whole skins behind them. Some were yet upon the way, pressing forward, without ever so much as

83

looking back; and these were all of them pale-faced, lean, thin, and miserably mortified. There was no passage that way for horsemen; and I was told that St. Paul himself left his horse when he went into it: and indeed there was not the footing of any beast to be seen, neither horse nor mule, nor the track of any coach or chariot; nor could I learn that any had ever passed that way. While I was thinking of what I had seen, I spied at length a beggar that was resting him a little to take breath; and I asked him what inns or lodgings they had upon that road? His answer was, that there was no stopping there, till they came to their journey's end: for this, said he, is the way to Paradise; and what should they do with inns or taverns where there are so few passengers? Do not you know that, in the course of nature, to die is to be born; to live is to travel; and the world is but a great inn, after which it is but one stage either to pain or glory? Thus saying, he marched forward, and bade me adieu; telling me withal, that it was time lost to linger in the way of virtue, and not safe to entertain such dialogues as tend rather to curiosity than instruction. He pursued his journey, stumbling, tearing his flesh, sighing and groaning at every step, and weeping, as if he thought to soften the stones with his tears. This is no way for me, thought I to myself, and no company neither; for they are a sort of beggarly morose people, and will never agree with my humour; so I drew back, and struck off into the left-hand road.

I found abundance of company in this way, and room for more. What a world of brave cavaliers! gilt coaches, rich liveries and handsome lively lasses, as glorious as the sun! Some were singing and laughing, others tickling one another and toying; some again at their sweetmeats and deserts, or appointing a set at cards: so that taking all together, I durst have sworn I had been at the Park. This minded me of an old saying, Tell me thy company and I will tell thee thy manners? and to save the credit of my education, I put myself into the fashion and jogged on. There in an instant I found myself up to the ears in balls, plays, masquerades, collations, dalliances, amours, and as full of joy as my heart could contain.

It was not here, as upon the other road, where folks were barefoot and naked, for want of shoemakers and tailors; for here were enough and to spare; besides mercers, drapers, jewellers, bodice-makers, peruke-makers, milliners, and a French ordinary at every other door. You cannot imagine the pleasure I took in my new acquaintance; and yet there was now and then some jostling and disorder upon the way chiefly between the physicians upon their mules, and the infantry of the lawyers, that marched in great bodies before the judges, and contested for a place. But the physicians carried it in favour of their charter, which gives them privilege to study, practice and teach the art of poisoning, and to read lectures upon it in the universities. While this point of honour was in dispute, I perceived several crossing from one way to the other, and changing parties; some of them stumbled and recovered; others fell downright: but the drollest gambol of all was that of the vintners; a whole litter of them tumbled into a pit together one over another; but finding they were out of their element, they got up again as fast as they could. Those that were in the right-hand way, which was the way to Paradise or Virtue, advanced very heavily, and made us excellent sport. Prithee look what a Friday-face that fellow makes, cries one; hang him, prick-eared cur, says another; dam'me, cries a third, if the rogue be not drunk with holy water; if the devil had raked hell, he could not have found such a pack of ill-looked rascals says another. Some of them stopped their ears, and went on without minding us; others we put out of countenance, and they came over to us; and a third sort came out of pure love to our company.

After this I saw a great many people afar off in a by-path, with as much contrition and devotion in their looks and gestures as ever I had seen in men: they walked shaking their heads, and lifting up their hands to heaven, and they had most of them large ears, and to my thinking Geneva Bibles. These, thought I, are a people of singular integrity and strictness of life above their fellows; but coming nearer, we found them to be hypocrites; and though they had none of our company upon the road, they would not fail to meet us at our journey's end. Fasting, repentance, prayer, mortification, and other holy duties, which are the exercise of good Christians, in order to their salvation, were but a kind of probation to these men, to fit them for the devil. They were followed by several devotees, and holy sisters, that kissed the skirts of their garments all the way they went, but whether out of zeal spiritual or natural, is hard to say; and undoubtedly some women's kisses are worse than that of Judas; for though his kiss was treacherous in the intention, it was yet right in the application: but this was one Judas kissing another; which makes me think there was more of the flesh than of the spirit in the case. Some were drawing a thread now and then out of the holy man's garment to make a relic of; others would cut out large snips, as if they had a mind to see them naked. Some again desired they would remember them in their prayers; which was just as much as if they had commended themselves to the devil by proxy. Some prayed for good matches for their daughters; others begged children for themselves; and sure the husband that allows his wife to ask children abroad, will be so civil as to take them home when they are given him. In short, these hypocrites may for a while, perhaps, impose upon all the world, and delude the multitude; but no mask or disguise is proof against the all-piercing eye of the Almighty. There are, I must own, many religious and godly men, for whose persons and prayers I have great esteem : but these are not of the hypocrite's humour, to build their hopes and ambition upon popular applause; and, with a counterfeit humility, to proclaim their weakness and un-worthiness, their failings, yea, and all their transgressions, in the market-place; all which, indeed, is but a truth, as they are really what they say, though they would not be thought so.

These went apart, and were looked upon to be neither fish nor flesh, nor good red-herring. They wore the name of Christians; but had neither the wit nor the honesty of Pagans; for they contented themselves with the pleasures of this life, because they knew no better; but the hypocrite that is instructed both in life temporal and eternal, lives without any comfort in the one, or hope in the other, and takes more pains to be damned, than a good Christian does to com-pass his salvation. In short, we went on our way in discourse. The rich followed their wealth, and the poor the rich, begging what Providence had denied them. The stubborn and obstinate went away by themselves; for they would hear nobody that was wiser than themselves, but rustled on, and pressed still to be foremost. The magistrates drew after them all the solicitors and attorneys. Corrupt judges were carried away by passion and avarice; and vain and ambitous princes trailed along by principalities and com-monwealths. There was a vast multitude of priests upon this road, too; and I saw one full regiment of soldiers there, which would have been brave fellows indeed, If they had been but half so good at praying and fighting as they were at swearing. Their whole discourse was one of their adventures; how narrowly they came off at such an assault; what wounds they received upon another breach, and then what destruction they made at such a time of sheep and poultry. But all they said came in at one ear, and went out at the other. Do not you remember, sirrah, says one, how we clawed it away at such a place? Yes, you rogue, cries the other, when you were so drunk you took your aunt for the bawd. These, and such as these, were the only exploits they could truly boast of.

While they were upon these glorious rhodomontades, certain generous spirits from the right-hand way, that knew what they were, by the boxes of passports, testimonials, and recommendations they wore at their girdles, cried out to them as if they had been to an attack, Fall on, fall on, my lads, and follow me; this, this is the path of honour; and, if you were not cowards, you would not quit it for fear of a fatiguing march, or an ill lodging. Courage, comrades, and be assured, that this combat, well fought, makes all your fortunes, and crowns you for ever. Here you shall be sure both of pay and reward, without casting the issue of your hazards and hopes upon the empty promises of princes. How long will you pursue this trade of blood and rapine, and accustom your ears and tongues to the tragical exclamations of burn, no quarter, kill or die? It is not pay, or pillage, but Virtue, that is a brave man's recompense: trust to her, and she will not deceive you. If it be war you love, come to us; bear arms on the right side, and we will find you work. Do not you know that a man's life is a warfare? that the world, the flesh, and the devil are three vigilant enemies? and that it is as much as his soul is worth to put himself, but for one minute, out of his guard? Princes tell you that your blood and your lives are theirs; and that to shed the one and lose the other, in their service, is no obligation, but a duty: you are still, however, to look to the cause; wherefore turn head, and come along with us, and be happy. The soldiers heard all this with exceeding patience and attention; but the brand of cowardice had such an effect upon them, that without any more ado, like men of honour, they presently wheeled about, drew, and, as bold as lions, charged headlong into a tavern.

After this we saw a troop of women upon the highway to hell, with their bags, and their fellows at their heels, ever and anon jostling one another. On the other side, a number of good people that were almost at the end of their journey, came over into the wrong road; for the right-hand way growing easier and wider towards the end, and that on the left-hand, on the contrary, narrower, they thought they had been out of the way, and so came into us: but as many of ours went over to them upon the same mistake. Among the rest, I saw a great lady, without either coach, sedan, or any living creature with her, foot it all the way to hell, which was to be so great a wonder, considering how she had lived in the world, that I presently looked for a public notary to make an entry of it. The woman was in a most miserable pickle; and I did not know what design she might drive on under that disguise; but finding never a notary or register at hand, though I missed my particular aim, yet I was well enough pleased, as I took it for granted that I was in my ready way to heaven: but when I came afterward to reflect upon the crosses, afflictions and mortifications that lie in the way to Paradise; and to consider that there was nothing of that upon this road; but on the contrary, laughing, singing, frolicking, and all manner of jollity this, I must own, gave me a qualm, and made me a little doubtful whither I was going.

I was quickly, however, delivered of that doubt by a gang of married men that we overtook, with their wives in their hands in evidence of their mortifications. My wife is my witness, cries one, that every day since I married her has been a fasting-day to me, to pamper her with broths and jellies; and my wife knows how I have humbled my body by nakedness; for I have hardly allowed myself a rag to my back, or a shoe to my foot, to maintain her in her coach, pages, gowns, petticoats, and jewels; so that, upon the whole, I perceive an unlucky hit with a wife gives a man as much right to the catalogue of martyrs as if he had ended his days at the stake.

The misery these poor wretches endured made me think myself in the right again, until I heard a cry behind me, Make way there, make way for the apothecaries. Bless me, thought I, if they be here, we are certainly going to the devil: and so it proved; for we were just then come to a little door that was made like a mouse-trap where it was easy to get in, but there was no getting out again.

It was very odd, that scarce anybody so much as dreamed of hell all the way we went, and yet everybody knew where they were as soon as they came there, and cried out with one voice, Miserable creatures! we are all damned, we are all damned. That word made my heart ache: And is it come to that, said I! Then did I begin, with tears in my eyes, to reflect upon what I had left in the world, as my relations, friends, ladies, mistresses, and, in a word, all my old acquaintance; when, with a heavy sigh, looking behind me, I saw a great part of them posting after me. It gave me, methought, some comfort, that I should have so good company, vainly imagining that even hell itself might be capable of some relief.

Proceeding farther on, I was gotten into a crowd of tailors that stood up sneaking in a corner for fear of the Devil. At the first door, there were seven devils taking the names of those that entered; and asking mine and my quality, they let me pass. But examining the tailors, These fellows, cried one of the devils, come in such crowds, as if hell was only made for tailors. How many are they? said another: answer was made, About a hundred. There must be more than a hundred, says the other, if they be tailors; for they never come under a thousand or twelve hundred strong; and we have so many of them here already, I know not where we shall stow them. Say the word, my masters, shall we let them in or no? The poor tailors were all trembling at that, for fear they should not get in; but in the end, they had the favour to be admitted. Certainly, said I, these folks are but in an ill condition, when it is a menace for the devils themselves to refuse to receive them. Thereupon, a huge, overgrown, club-footed, crump-shouldered devil, threw them into a deep hole. Seeing such a monster of a devil, I asked him how to came to be so deformed; he told me he had spoiled his back with carrying tailors : for, said he, I have been made use of as a sumpter to fetch them; but now of late they save me that labour, and come so fast of themselves, that it is one devil's work to dispose of them. While he was yet speaking, there came another glut of them; and I was obliged to make way, that the devil might have room to get in, who piled them up, and told me, they made the best fuel in hell.

I passed forward then into a little dark alley, where it made me start to hear one call me by my name, and, with much ado, I perceived a fellow there all wrapped up in smoke and flame.

Alas Sir, says he, have you forgot your old bookseller in the Strand? I cry thee mercy, good Livewell, said I : what! art thou here? Yes, yes, Sir, says he, it is even too true; I never dreamt it would have come to this. He thought I must needs pity him, when I knew him; but truly I reflected rather upon the justice of his punishment; for, in a word, his shop was the very mint of heresy, schism, and sedition. I put on a face of compassion, however, to give him a little ease, which he took hold of, and thus vented his complaint : "Well, Sir, says he, I would rather my father had made me a hangman when he made me a bookseller; for we are called to account for other men's works as well as for our own; and one thing cast in our dish is, the selling of translations so dog cheap, that every sot knows now as much as would formerly have made a passable doctor; nay, every groom and valet is grown as familiar with Homer, Virgil, and Ovid, as with the seven Champions, or Robinson Crusoe. He would have talked on, if a devil had not stopped his mouth with a whiff from a roll of his own papers, and choked him with the smoke of it. The pestilent fume would have despatched me too if I had not got presently out of reach. But I went my way, saying this to myself : If the bookseller be thus criminal, how guilty must the author be.

I was delivered from this meditation by the rueful groans of several souls that were under the lash, and the devils tyrannizing over them with whips and scourges. I inquired what they were? And it was told me, that there was a plot among the hackney-coachmen to exhibit an information against the devils, for taking the whip out of their hands, and setting up a trade they had never served their time to, which is directly contrary to the statute. Well, said I, what are these tormented here? With that an old sour-looking coachman took the answer out of the devil's mouth, and told me, That it was because they came to hell on horseback, which they pretended was a privilege that did not belong to rogues of their quality. Speak truth, and be hanged, cried the devil, and make an honest confession here. Say, sirrah, how many bawdy journeys have you made to Hackney? How many nights have you stood pimping at Vauxhall? How many whores and knaves have you brought together? And how many lies have you told to keep all private, since you first set up this scandalous trade? There was a coachman near who had served a judge, and thought it was no more for his old master to fetch a rascal out of hell than out of Newgate; which made this fellow stand upon his points, and ask the devil how he durst give that language to so honourable a profession; for, says he, who is better dressed than your coachmen? Are we not in our velvets, embroideries, and laces? and as glorious as so many Phætons? Have not our masters reason to be good to us, when their necks are at stake, and their lives at our mercy? Nay, we govern those many times that govern kingdoms: a prince is in almost as much danger of his coachman as of his physician; and there are those who understand it too, and themselves, and us; and who will not stick to trust their coachmen as far as they would do their confessors. There is no absurdity in the comparison; for if they know some of their privacies, we know more: yes, and perhaps more tthan we will speak of. What have we here to do? cried a devil that was ready to split his sides with laughing; a coachman in his tropes and figures; an orator instead of a waggoner? The slave has broken his bridle, and got his head at liberty, and now he will never have done. No, why should he? says another that had served a lady more ways than one, is this the best entertainment you can afford your servants, your daily drudges? I am sure we bring you a good commodity, well packed, well conditioned, well perfumed, right, neat and clean; not like your city-ware, that comes dirty to you, up to the knees; and yet every draggle-tail wench and skip-kennel shall be better used than we. Ah! the ingratitude of this place! If we had done as much for somebody else as we have done for you, we should not have been now to seek for our wages. When you have nothing else to say, you tell me that I am punished for carrying the sick, the gouty, the lame, to church, to mass; or some straggling virgins back again to their cloister; which is a great falsehood; for I am able to prove that all my trading lies at the play-houses, bawdy-houses, taverns, balls, collations; or else at the tour a-la-mode, where there was still appointed some after-meeting, to treat of certain affairs, that highly import the interest and welfare of your dominions. I have indeed carried my mistress sometimes to the church door, but it signified no more than if I had carried her to a conventicle; for all her business there was to meet her gallant, and to agree when they should meet next, according to the way of devotion now in fashion. In a word, it is most certain that I never took any creature, knowingly, into my coach, that had so much as a good thought; and this was so well known, that it was all one to ask if a lady were a maid, or if she had ever been in my coach. If it appeared she had, he that married her knew beforehand what he had to trust to. And, after all this, how excellently have you rewarded us! With that the devil fell a-laughing; and, with five or six twinging jerks, half-flayed the poor coachman; so that I was very glad to retire; in pity partly to the coachman and partly to myself; for the currying of a coachman is little better than the turning up of a dunghill.

I next went into a deep vault, where I began immediately to shudder, and my teeth chattered in my head. I asked the meaning of it; and there came up to me a devil with kibed heels and his toes all mortified, who told me that that quarter was allotted to buffoons and drolls, which are a people, says he, of so starved a conceit, and so cold a discourse, that we are obliged to chain and lock them up, for fear they should spoil the temper of our fire. I asked if a man might see them. The devil told me, yes; and showed me one of the lewdest kennels in hell. There were they at it, pecking at one another, and playing the same fooleries over and over again that they had practised upon earth. Among the buffoons I saw several that passed here in the world for men of honesty and honour; which were in, as the devil told me, for flattery; and were a species of buffoons that goes betwixt the bark and the tree. But why are they condemned? said I. The other buffoons are condemned, replied the devil, for want of favour, and these for having too much and abusing it. You must know they come upon us still at unawares; and yet they find all things in readiness; the cloth laid, and the bed made, as if they were at home. To say the truth, we have some art of kindness for them; for they save us a great deal of trouble in tormenting one another.

Do you see him there? That was a wicked and partial judge; and all he has to say for himself is, That he remembers the time when he could have broke the neck of two honest causes, though he put them only out of joint. That good fellow there was a careless husband, and him we lodge too with the buffoons. He sold his wife's portion, wife and all, to please his companions, and turned both into an annuity. That lady there, though a great one, is obliged to take up with the buffoons, for they are both of humour: what they do with their talk, she does with her body, and seasons it to all appetites. In short, you shall find buffoons in all conditions; and in effect, there are nigh as many as there are men and women; for the whole world is given to jeering, slandering, backbiting; and there are more natural buffoons than artificial.

At my leaving the vault, I saw near a thousand devils following a drove of pastry cooks, and breaking their heads as they passed along with iron peels. Alas! cried one of them, that was yet in whole skin, it is hard the sin of the flesh should be laid to our charge, that never had to do with women. Impudent rascals, cried the devil, who has deserved hell, if you have not? How many thousand men have such slovens poisoned with the grease of their heads, and tallow instead of mutton suet? With kitchen-stuff pies for marrow? and flies for currants? How many stomachs have they turned into laystals with dogs-flesh, horse-flesh, and other carrion, that they have put into them? and yet do these rogues complain, in the devil's name, of their sufferings! Leave your bawling, ye ragamuffins, continues he, and know that the pain you endure is nothing to that of your tormenters. And for your part, says he to me, with a sour look, because you are a stranger you may go about your business; but we have a crow to pluck with these fellows before we have done.

I descended next a pair of stairs which lead to a huge cellar, where I saw men burning in unquenchable fire; and one of them roaring, cried out, I never over-sold, I never sold but at conscionable rates; why am I punished thus? I durst have sworn it had been Judas; but going nearer to him to see if he had a red head, I found him to be a merchant of my acquaintance that died not long since. How now, old Martin, said I, art thou here? He was dogged, because I did not call him Sir, and made no answer. I saw his grief, and told him how much he was to blame to cherish that vanity, even in hell, which had brought him thither. And what do you think of it now? said I; had not you better have traded in blacks than Christians? Had not you better have contented yourself with a little honestly got, than run the hazard of your soul for an estate; and have gone to heaven on foot, rather than to the devil on horseback? My friend was as mute as a fish; whether out of anger, shame or grief, I know not. And then a devil in office took up the discourse: These cheating rascals, says he, did they think to govern the world with their own weights and measures, in *secula seculorum*? Methinks the blinking and false lights of their shops should have minded them of their quarter in this world beforehand; and it is all a case with jewellers, goldsmiths, and other trades, that serve only to flatter and bolster up the world in luxury and folly. But if people would be wise, these youths should have little enough to do. For what is their cloth of gold and silver, their silks, their diamonds, and pearls, which they sell at their own price, but mere wantonness and superfluity? These are they that inveigle men into all manner of extravagant expenses, and so ruin them insensibly, under pretence of kindness and credit, for they set everything at double the rate; and if their creditors keep not touch at a day, their persons are imprisoned, their goods seized, and their estates extended; and they that helped to make a prince before are now the forwardest to put the wretch into the condition of a beggar.

The Devil would have talked on if I had given him the hearing; but there was such a laugh set up on one side of me as if they would all have split, and I went to see what the matter was; for it was a strange thing, methought, to hear them so merry in hell. The business was, there were two men upon a scaffold, in genteel habits, hallooing with all their might. One of them had a great parchment in his hand displayed, with divers labels hanging at it, and several seals. I thought at first it might have been execution-day, and took the writing for a pardon or reprieve. At every word they spoke, a matter of seven or eight thousand devils burst out a-laughing, as if they would have cracked their sides; and this again made me think it might be some Merry Andrew, or mountebank, showing his tricks or his attestations, with his congregation of fools about him; but nearer I found my mistake, and that the devils mirth made the gentlemen angry. At last I perceived that this great earnestness of theirs was only to make out their pedigree, and get themselves to pass for gentlemen; the parchment being a testimonial from the herald's office to that purpose. My father, says he, with the writing in his hand, bore arms for his majesty on many honourable occasions, in watching and warding; and has made many a tall fellow speak to the constable at all hours of the night. My uncle was the first man that ever was of the order of St. James; and we have had five brave commanders of our family, by my father's side, that have served the state in the quality of marshal's men and turnkeys, and given his majesty a fair account of all the prisoners committed to their charge: and by my mother's side, it cannot be denied but that I am honourably descended; for my grandmother was never without a dozen chambermaids and nurses in the family. Perhaps it was her trade, cried the Devil, to procure services and servants, and consequently to deal in that commodity. Well, well, said the cavalier, she was what she was; and I am sure I tell you nothing but truth. Her husband wore a sword by his place, for he was a deputy-marshal; and, to prove myself a man of honour, I have it here in black and white, under the seal of the office. Why must I then be quartered among a pack of rascals? My gentleman, replied the Devil, your grandfather wore a sword as he was usher to a fencing-school; and we know very well what his son and grandchild can pretend to. But let that pass; you have led a wicked and infamous life, and spent your time in whoring, drinking and blaspheming, and in lewd company; and do you tell us now of the privileges of your nobility; your testimonials, and the seal of the office, and all? there is no honour but virtue; and if your children, though they had a scoundrel to their father, should come to do honourable and worthy things, we should look upon them as persons sacred, and not dare to meddle with them. But talking is to no purpose; you were always a couple of pitiful fellows, and your tails are scarce worth the scalding. Have at you then, says he; and at the word, with a huge iron bar he gave them such a salute over the buttocks, that they took two or three turns in the air, heels over head, and dropped at last into the common sewer, where never any man has yet found the bottom.

When his companions had seen him cut that caper, This usage, says one of them, may be well enough for a parchment gentleman; but a cavalier of my extraction and profession I suppose you will treat somewhat more respectfully. Cavalier, cried the Devil, if you have brought no better plea along with you than the antiquity of your house, you may even follow your comrade for aught I know; we find very few ancient families that had not some oppressor or usurper for their founder; and they are commonly continued by the same means they were begun. How many are there of our titular nobility that write noble purely upon account of their violence and injustice? Their subjects and tenants, what with impositions, hard services, and racked rents, are they not worse than slaves? If they happen to have anything extraordinary (as a pleasant fruit, a handsome colt, or a fat cow), and the landlord or his sweet lady take a liking to it, they must either submit or part with it gratis, or else take their pay in foul language, or even blows: and it is well if they escape so; for very often, when the sign is in Gemini, their wives and daughters go to pot, without any regard of laws either sacred or profane. What horrid blasphemies do they make use of to get credit with a mistress or a creditor upon a faithless promise! How intolerable is their pride and insolence, even towards many considerable officers, both in church and state! They behave themselves as if all people below their quality and rank in the world were but as so many brutes, or worse, as if human blood were not all of a colour; as if nature had not brought them into the world the common way, or moulded them of the same materials with the meanest wretches upon the earth. And then, for such as have military charges and commands, how many great officers are there, that, without any consideration of their own or their prince's honour, fall to spoil and to pillage, defrauding the state with false musters, cheating the soldiers of their pay, and giving them, instead of their due from the prince, a liberty of taking what is not their due from the people; forcing them to take the bread out of the poor labourers mouths, to fill their own bellies; and protecting them, when they have done, in the most execrable outrages imaginable : and, that the poor soldier comes at last to be dismissed or disbanded, lame, sick, beggarly, almost naked, and with nothing left him to trust to, but the highway to keep him from starving; what mischief is there in the world that these men is not the cause of? How many good families are entirely ruined and at this day in the hospital, for trusting to their oaths and promises, and becoming bound for them for vast sums of money to maintain them in drink and whores, and in every species of luxury and riot? This rhetorical devil would have said a thousand times more, but that his companions called him off, and told him they had business elsewhere. The cavalier hearing that, My friend, said he, your morals are very good; but yet, with your favour, all men are not alike. There is never a barrel the better herring, said the Devil, you are all of you tainted with original sin, and if you had been any better than your fellows, you had never been sent to this place. But if you are indeed so noble as you say, you are worth the burning, if it were but for your ashes; and that you may have no cause of complaint, you shall see that we treat you like a person of condition. At that instant two devils presented themselves, the one bridled and saddled, and the other doing the office of the squire, holding the stirrup with his left hand and giving the gentleman a lift into the saddle with the other. This was no sooner done, but away he went like an arrow out of a bow. I asked the Devil then into what country he carried him : and he told me not far, for it was only matter of decorum, to send the nobility to hell on horseback. Turn your eyes to that side now, says he. I did so, and there I saw the poor cavalier in a huge furnace, with the first inventors of nobility and arms; as Cain, Cham, Nimrod, Esau, Romulous, Tarquin, Nero, Caligula, Domitian, Heliogabalus, and several other brave fellows, that had made themselves famous by usurpation and blood. The place was a little too hot for me, therefore I retired, meditating on what I had heard, and not a little satisfied with the discourse of so learned a devil. Till that time, I imagined the devil was a notorious liar, but I find now that he can speak the truth when he thinks proper, and I would not for all I am worth but have heard him preach.

When I was thus far, my curiosity carried me still farther; and, within twenty yards I came to a large muddy stinking lake, nearly twice as big as that of Geneva, and heard in it so strange a noise that I was almost out of my wits to know what it was. They told me that the lake was stored with duegnas, which are metamorphosed into a kind of frogs in hell, and continually spluttering and croaking. Methought the conversion was apt enough, for they are neither fish nor flesh, no more than frogs, and only the lower parts of them are men's meat; but their heads are enough to turn a very good stomach; I could not but laugh to see how they gaped, and stretched out their legs as they swam; and still, as we came nearer, they scudded away and dived to the bottom.

There was so poisonous a vapour in this place, that I was obliged to leave it, and I struck off to the left hand, where I saw several old men beating their breasts and tearing their faces, with bitter groans and lamentations. It made my heart ache to see them, and I asked what they were? I was informed that I was now in the quarters of the Fathers that damned themselves to raise their posterity, which are called by some, the Unadvised. Wretch that I am! cried one; the greatest penitent that ever lived, never suffered the mortification I have endured; I have watched, I have fasted, I have scarce had any clothes on my back; my whole life has been a restless course of torment, both of body and mind, and all this to get money for my children, that I might see them well married, purchase them posts at court, or procure them some other preferment in the world; starving myself in the conclusion, rather than I would lessen the provision I had made for my posterity : and yet, notwithstanding this my fatherly care, I was scarce sooner dead than forgotten; and my next heir buried me without tears or mourning, and indeed without so much as paying my legacies, or praying for my soul, as if they had received certain intelligence of my damnation. To increase my misery, the prodigals are now squandering and consuming that estate in gaming, whoring and debauches, which I had gained by so much industry, vexation and oppression, for which I suffer at this instant such insupportable torments. This should have been thought on before, said a devil; for sure you have heard of the old saying, Happy the child whose father goes to the devil. At which word, the old miser broke out into fresh lamentation, tearing his flesh in so rueful a manner, that I could no longer bear the sight.

A little farther, there was a dismal gloomy dungeon, where I heard the clattering of chains, the crackling of flames, the smacking of whips, and a confused outcry of complaints. I asked what quarter this was; and they told me it was the quarter of the late repentants. What are those? said I. Answer was made, that they were a company of brutish sots, so absolutely delivered up to vice that they were damned insensible, and in hell before they knew anything of the matter. They are now reflecting upon their miscarriages and omissions, and continually crying out, Oh that I had examined my conscience! Oh that I had frequented the sacraments! Oh that I had humbled myself with fasting and prayer! Oh that I had served God as I ought! Oh that I had visited the sick and been charitable to the poor! Oh that I had set a watch before the door of my lips!

I left these late repentants, as it appeared, in exchange for worse, which were confined in a low court, and the nastiest that ever I saw. These were such as had continually in their mouth, God is merciful and will pardon me. How can this be, said I, that these people should be damned, when condemnation is an act of justice, not of mercy? I perceive you are simple, cried the Devil; for half these you see here are condemned with the mercy of God in their mouths; and, to explain myself, consider, I beseech ye, how many sinners are there that go on in their ways, in spite of reproof and good counsel; and still this is their answer, God is merciful, and will not damn a soul for such a trifle. But let them talk of mercy as they please, so long as they persist in a wicked life we are like to have their company at last. By your argument, said I, there is no trusting to Divine Mercy. You mistake me, cried the Devil; for every good thought and work flows from that mercy. But this I say, he that perseveres in his wickedness, and makes use of the name of mercy, only to palliate his impieties, does but mock the Almighty, and has no title to that mercy. For it is in vain to expect mercy from above without doing anything in order to obtain it. It properly belongs to the righteous and the penitent; and they that have the most of it upon the tongue, have commonly the least thought of it in their hearts: and it is a great aggravation of guilt to sin the more in confidence of an abounding mercy. I must own that several are received to mercy who are utterly unworthy of it; which is no wonder; no man of himself can deserve it: but men are so careless of seeking it by times that they put that off to the last, which should have been the first part of their business; and frequently their life is at an end before they begin their repentance. I was struck to hear so damned a doctor make so good a sermon; but there I left him.

I came next to a noisome dark hole, where I beheld a company of dyers, all in dirt and smoke, intermixed with the devils, and so alike, that it would have puzzled the subtilest inquisitor in Spain to have distinguished them.

I perceived at my elbow an odd kind of mongrel devil, begot betwixt a black and a white, with a head so bestuck with little horns, that at a distance it had the appearance of a hedgehog. I had the boldness to ask him where they quartered the Sodomites, the old women and the cuckolds? As for cuckolds, said

G

he, they are all over hell, without any certain quarter or station: and in truth, it is no easy matter to know a cuckold from a devil; for like kind husbands, they wear their wives' favours still, and the very same headpieces in hell that they wore while upon earth. As to the Sodomites, we have no more to do with them than needs must; but upon all occasions we either fly or face them: for, if ever we come to give them a broadside, it is ten to one but we get a hit between wind and water; and yet we fence with our tails as well as we can, and they get now and then a slap over the mouth into the bargain. And for the old women, we make them stand off; for we take as little pleasure in them as you do: and yet the jades will be persecuting us with their passions; and ye shall have a bawd of fifty-five do all the gambols of a girl of fifteen; yet, after all this, there is not an old woman in hell; for, let her be as old as you please, bald, blind, toothless, wrinkled and decrepid; this is not her age, she will tell you, but by a terrible fit of sickness last year, that fetched off her hair and brought her so low, that she has not yet recovered her flesh again. She lost her eyes by a hot rheum; and utterly spoiled her teeth by cracking of peach-stones, and eating of sweetmeats when she was a maid; and, when the weight of her years has almost brought both ends together, it is nothing, she will tell you, but a crick she has got in her back: and though she might recover youth again by confessing her age, yet she always denies it.

My attention next was taken up with a number of people making their moan, that they had been carried off by sudden death. That is an arrant lie, cried a devil, saving this gentleman's presence, for no man dies suddenly; Death surprises no man, but gives all men sufficient warning and notice. I was much taken with the devil's civility and discourse, which he thus continued. Do you complain, says he, of sudden death, that have carried death about you ever since you were born; that have been entertained with daily spectacles of carcasses and funerals; that have heard so many sermons upon the subject, and read so many books upon the frailty of life, and the certainty of death? Are you not sensible that every moment ye live brings ye nearer to your end? your clothes wear out, your woods and your houses decay, and yet ye hope that your bodies should be immortal. What are the common accidents and diseases of life, but so many warnings to provide yourself for a remove? Ye have death at your table in your daily food and nourishment; for your life is maintained by the death of other creatures; and you have the lively picture of it every night for your bed-fellow. With what face, then, can you change your misfortune upon sudden death, who have spent your whole life both at bed and board, among so many remembrances of your mortality? No, no; change your style, and hereafter confess yourselves to have been careless and incredulous. Ye die, thinking you are not to die yet, and forgetting that death grows upon you, and goes along with ye, from one end of your life to the other, without distinguishing of persons or ages, sex or quality, and whether it finds you well or ill-doing; as the tree falls, so it lies.

Turning towards my left hand, I beheld several souls that were put up in gallipots, with affa-fœtida, galbanum, and a company of oils that served them for syrup. What a confounded stink is here! cried I, stopping my nose; we are now come undoubtedly to the devil's necessary-house. No, no, said the tormentor, which was a kind of yellowish complexioned devil, it is a confection of apothecaries: a sort of people that are commonly damned for compounding the medicines by which their patients hope to be saved. To give them their due, these are your only true and chemical philosophers, and worth a thousand of Raymund, Lullies, Hermes, Geber, Ruspicella, Avicen and their fellows. It is true; they have written excellent things of the transmutation of metals, but did they ever make gold? or, if they did, we have lost the secret. Whereas, your apothecaries, out of a little puddle-water, a bundle of rotten sticks, a box of flies, nay, out of toads, vipers, and a fir—reverence itself, shall fetch ye gold ready minted, and fit for the market; which is more than all your philosophical projectors ever pretended to. There is no herb so poisonous, nor any stone so dry, not even the pumice itself, but they will extract silver from it: and then, for words, it is impossible to make up any word out of the four-and-twenty letters, but they will show you a drug or a plant of the name; and turn the alphabet into as good money as any in your pocket. Ask them for an eyetooth of a flying toad, they will tell ye, Yes ye may have it in powder; or if you had rather have the infusion of a tench of the mountains, in a little eel's milk, it is all one to them. If there be but any money stirring, you shall have what you will, though there be no such thing in nature. So that it looks as if all the plants and stones in the creation had their several powers and virtues given them only for the apothecaries sakes; and as if words themselves had been only made for their advantage. Ye call them apothecaries, but, instead of that, I prithee, call them armourers and their shops arsenals. Are not their medicines as certain death as swords, daggers, or muskets; while their patients are purged and blooded into the other world, without any regard either to distemper, measure, or season?

If you will now behold the most diverting sight you have seen yet, walk but up these two steps, and you shall see a jury, or conspiracy, of barber-surgeons sitting upon life and death. You must think that any amusement there was welcome; so I went up, and found it, I must own, a very pleasant spectacle. These barbers were most of them chained by the middle, their hands at liberty, and every one of them had a cittern about his neck, and upon his knees a chess-board, and still as he reached to have a touch at the cittern, the instrument vanished; as also did the chess-board, when he thought to have a game at draughts. This was directly tantalizing the poor rogues; for a cittern is as natural to a barber as milk to a calf. Some of them were washing asses brains and putting them in again; and scourging negroes to make them white.

When I had laughed my fill at these fooleries, my next discovery was of a vast multitude of people, grumbling and muttering that there was nobody to look after them; no, not so much as to torment them; as if their tails were not as well worth the toasting as their neighbours. Answer was made, That, being a kind of devils themselves, they might put in for some sort of authority in the place, and execute the office of tormentors. This made me ask what they were? and a devil very respectfully told me that they were a company of ungracious, left-handed wretches, that could do nothing aright, and their grievance was that they were quartered by themselves: but not knowing whether they were men or no, or indeed what else to make of them, we did not know how to match them, or in what company to put them. In the world they are looked upon as ill omens; and let any man meet one of them upon a journey in a morning, fasting, it is the same thing as if a hare had crossed his way; for he presently turns his head in discontent, and goes to bed again. You know that Scævola, when he found his mistake in killing another for Porsenna, the secretary for the prince, burnt his right hand in revenge for the miscarriage. Now the severity of the vengeance was not so much the maiming or the crippling of himself, as the condemning himself to be forever left-handed. And so it is with a malefactor that suffers justice; the shame and punishment does not lie so much in the loss of his right-hand, as that the other is left. And it was the curse of an old bawd, to a fellow who had provoked her, that he might go to the devil by the stroke of a left-handed man. If the poets speak truth, as it were a wonder if they should not, the left is the unlucky side, and there never came any good from it. And, for my last argument against these creatures, the goats and reprobates stand upon the left-hand; and left-handed men are, in short, a sort of creature that is made to do mischief; nay, whether I should call them men or no, I know not.

Hereupon a devil made a sign to me to come softly to him, which I did, without speaking a word, or making the least noise. Now, says he, if you will see the daily exercise of ill-favoured women, look through that lattice-window. There I saw such a crowd of ugly creatures, as you would have blessed yourself to avoid them. Some with their faces so pounced and speckled, as if they had been scarrified, and newly passed the cupping-glass, with a world of little plasters, long, round, square; and briefly cut out into such a variety, that it would have perplexed a good mathematician to find out another figure; and you would have sworn that they had been either at cats-play or cuffs. Others were scraping their faces with pieces of glass, tearing up their eyebrows by the roots like mad; and some that had none to tear, were fetching out of their black boxes such as they could get or make: others were powdering and curling the false locks, or fastening their new ivory teeth in the place of their old ebony ones. Some were chewing lemon-peel or cinnamon, to disguise a foul breath, and raising themselves upon their heels, that their view might be the fairer and their fall the deeper: others were quarrelling with their looking-glasses for showing them such ugly faces, and cursing the state of Venice for entertaining no better workmen: some were stuffing out their bodies like pack-saddles to conceal secret deformities: and some again had so many hoods over their faces to conceal their ruins, that I could hardly discern what they were; and these passed for penitents: others, with pots of pomatum, were sleeking and polishing their faces; and indeed their foreheads were bright and shining, though there were neither suns nor stars in that firmament: some there were, in fine, that would have made a man sick to see them at their cosmetic employments. Well, cried the Devil, you see now how far a woman's wit and invention will carry her to her own destruction. I could not speak one word for astonishment at so horrid a spectacle till I had a little recollected myself: but then answered, If I may deal freely without offence, I dare defy all the devils in hell to surpass these women: let us be gone, for the sight of them makes my very heart ache.

Turn about then, said the Devil: I obeyed, and beheld a fellow sitting in a chair, all alone, never a devil near him: no fire, no frost, no heat or cold, or anything else that I could perceive, to torment him; and yet crying and roaring out the most hideously of anything that I had yet heard in hell; tearing his flesh and beating his body, like a madman; and his heart all the while bleeding at his eyes. Good Lord, thought I, what is the matter with this wretch, that he yells out thus when nobody hurts him! Friend, said I, what is the meaning of all this fury and transport? For, so far as I can see, there is nothing to trouble You. No, no, says he, with a horrid outcry, and all the extravagances of a man

in rage and despair, you do not see my tormentors; but the all searching eye of
the Almighty sees my pains as well as my transgressions; and, with a severe and
implacable justice, has condemned me to suffer punishments suitable to my
crimes: which words he uttered with redoubled clamours. My executioners are
in my soul, and all the plagues of hell in my conscience: my memory serves me
instead of a cruel devil: the remembrance of the good I should have done, and
omitted, and of ill I should not have done, and did: the remembrance of the
salutary counsels I have rejected, and of the ill-example I have given: and, for
the aggravation of my misery, where my memory leaves afflicting me, my under-
taking begins, showing me the glories and happiness I have lost, which others
enjoy, who have gained heaven with less anxiety and pain, than I have endured
to compass my damnation. Now am I always meditating on the comforts, beauties, felicities and raptures of Paradise, only to inflame and exasperate my
despair in hell; begging, to no purpose, but for one moment's interval of ease,
without obtaining any; for my will is also as inexorable as either my memory
or my understanding. And these, my friend, are the three faculties of my soul;
which Divine Justice, for my sins, has converted into three tormentors, that
silently torture me; these the three flames that burn me without consuming. And
if I chance at any time to have the least remission or respite, the worm of my
conscience gnaws my soul, and gives it an insatiable hunger to an immortal
aliment. At that word, turning towards me with a hellish yell, Mortal, said he,
learn, and be assured from me, that all those that either bury or misemploy
their talents carry a hell within themselves, and are damned even above ground.
Upon this I left him, very pensive. Well, thought I, what a weight of sin lies
upon this creature's conscience! Whereupon the devil observing me in a pause,
told me in my ear that this fellow had been an atheist, and believed neither
God nor devil. Preserve me then, said I, from that unsanctified wisdom, which
serves us only for our farther condemnation.

I had hardly gone a step or two aside, when I saw a multitude of people
running after burning chariots, with a great many fools in them, and the devils
tearing them with pincers; and before them marched certain officers, making
proclamation of their sentence; which with much ado I got near enough to hear,
and it was to this effect: Divine Justice hath appointed this punishment to the
scandalous, for giving ill-examples to their neighbours! At the same time several
of the damned laid their sins to their charge, and cried out that it was owing
to them they were thus tormented; so that the scandalous were punished for
their own sins, and for the offences of those they had misled to their destruc-

tion. And these are they of whom it is said, "that they had better never been born !"

I was very sorry at the sight of so many melancholy spectacles; and yet I could not but smile to see the vintners everywhere up and down hell, as free as if they had been in their taverns, and only prisoners upon parole. I asked how they came by that privilege? A devil told me there was no need of shackling them, or so much as shutting them up; for there was no fear of their making their escape, as they took so much pains in the world, and made it their whole business to come hither. Only, says he, if we can prevent them from throwing water in the fire, as they do in their wine, we are well enough. But, if you would see somewhat worth while, leave these fellows and follow me; and I will show you Judas and his brethren, the stewards and purse-bearers. I obeyed him, and he brought me to Judas and his companions, who had many of them no faces, and most of them no foreheads.

I was well enough pleased to see him, and to be better informed; for I had always imagined him to be a kind of an olive-coloured, tawny-complexioned fellow, without a beard, and an eunuch into the bargain : which, perhaps, nay, probably, he was; for nothing but a castrato, a thing unmanned, could ever be guilty of so sordid and treacherous a villainy as to sell and betray his Master with a kiss : and, after that, so cowardly as to hang himself in despair when he had done. I do believe, however, what the church says of him, that he had a carrot-beard and a red head; but it may be his beard was burnt; and, as he appeared to me in hell I could not but take him for an eunuch; which, to deal freely, is my opinion of all the devils; for they have no hair, and they are for the most part wrinkled and bow-legged.

Judas was in the midst of a vast crowd of money-mongers and purse-bearers, that were telling him stories of the pranks they had played, and the tricks they had put upon their masters, after his example. Coming up to them, I perceived that their punishment was like that of Titius, who had a vulture continually gnawing upon his liver; for there were a multitude of ravenous birds constantly gnawing them and tearing off their flesh, which grew again as fast as they devoured it : a devil, in the meantime, crying out, and the damned filling the whole place with clamour and horror; Judas, with his purse and his pot by his side, bearing large part in the outcry and torment. I had a huge mind, me-thought, to have a word or two with Judas, and so I went to him with this greeting : Thou perfidious, impudent, impious traitor, said I, to sell thy Lord and Master at so base a price, like an avaricious villain. If men, said he, were not ungrateful, they would rather pity, or commend me, for an action so much to their advantage, and done in order to their redemption. The misery is mine, that I am to have no part myself in the benefit I have procured to others. Some heretics there are, I must own to my comfort, that esteem me for it. But do you take me for the only Judas? No, no, there have been several since the death of my Master: and there are, at this day, more wicked and ungrateful ten thousand times than myself, that buy the Lord of life as well as sell him; scourging and crucifying him daily with more spite and ignominy than the Jews. The truth is, I had an itch to be fingering of money, and bartering, from my very entrance into the apostleship. I began, you know, with the pot of ointment, which I would fain have sold, under pretence of a relief to the poor: and I went on to the selling my Master; wherein I did the world a greater good than I intended, to my own irreparable ruin. My repentance now is to no purpose. In a word, I am the only steward that is condemned for selling; all the rest are damned for buying: and I must entreat you to have a better opinion of me; for, if you look but a little lower here, you will find people far worse than myself. Withdraw then, said I, for I have discoursed enough with Judas.

I therefore descended some few steps, as Judas commanded me; and there I saw a world of devils upon the march, with rods and stirrup-leathers in their hands, lashing a company of handsome lasses, stark naked, and driving them out of hell, which methought was a pity; and if I had had some of them in a corner I should have treated them better. With the stirrup-leathers they disciplined a litter of bawds. I could not imagine why these of all others should be expelled the place, and asked the question. Oh, replies a devil, these are our factresses in the world, and the best we have; so that we send them back again to bring more grist to the mill: and, indeed, if it were not for women, hell would be but thinly peopled; for, what with the art, the beauty, and the allurements of the young wenches, and the sage advice and counsel of the bawds, they do us very good service. Nay, for fear any of our good friends should weary upon the road, they send them to us on horseback, or bring them themselves, even to the very gate, lest they should miss their way.

Pursuing my journey, I beheld at a distance a large building that looked, methought, like some enchanted castle, or the picture of ill-luck. It was all in ruin: the chimneys down, the floors all to pieces, and only the bars of the windows standing: the doors were all bedaubed with dirt, and patched up with barrel-heads, where they had been broken: the glass gone, and here and there a pane supplied with paper. I made no doubt at first but the house was forsaken;

but coming nearer I found it otherwise, by a horrible confusion of tongues and noises within it. As I came just up to the door, one opened it, and I saw in the house many devils, thieves and whores. One of the craftiest jades in the pack placed herself presently on the threshold, and thus addressed my guide and me: Gentleman, says she, how comes it to pass, I pray, that people are damned both for giving and taking? The thief is condemned for taking away from another, and we are condemned for giving what is our own: I do not find, truly, an injustice in our trade; and if it be lawful to give everyone their own, and out of their own, why are we condemned? We found it a nice point, and sent the wench to counsel learned in the law, for a resolution in the case. Her mentioning of thieves made me enquire after the scriveners and notaries. Is it possible, said I, that you should have none of them here? for I do not remember that I have seen so much as one of them upon the way; and yet I had occasion for a scrivener, and made a search for one. I do believe, indeed, said the Devil, that you have not found any of them upon the road. What, cried I, are they all saved? No, no, replied the Devil; but you must understand that they do not foot it hither, as other mortals, but come upon the wing, in troops, like wild-geese; so that it is no wonder you saw none of them upon the way. We have millions of them, but they speed it away in a trice; for they will make a flight, in the third part of a minute, betwixt earth and hell. But if there be so many, said I, how comes it we see none of them? For that, replied the Devil, we change their names when they come hither, and call them no longer notaries, or scriveners, but cats: and they are so good mousers, that though this place is large, old, and ruinous, yet you see not so much as a rat or mouse in hell, how full soever of all other kinds of vermin. Now ye talk of vermin, said I, are there any catchpoles here? No, not one says he. How so? cried I, when I dare under-take there are five hundred rogues of the trade, for one that is honest. The reason is, says the Devil, that every catchpole upon earth carries a hell in his bosom. You have still, said I, crossing myself, an aching tooth at these poor varlets. Why not, cried he, for they are but devils incarnate, and so well versed in the art of tormenting, that we live in continual dread of losing our places, lest his Infernal Majesty should take these rascals into his service.

I had enough of this; and, pursuing my journey, I saw a little way off a great enclosure, and a world of souls shut up in it; some of them weeping and lamenting without measure, and others in profound silence: this I understood to be the lovers quarter. It made me melancholy to consider that death itself could not kill the lamentations of lovers. Some of them were discoursing of their

passions, and teasing themselves with fears and jealousies; casting all their
miseries upon their appetites and fancies, which still made the picture infinitely
fairer than the person. They were, for the most part, troubled with a simple
disease, called, as the Devil told me, Thought. I asked him what that was; and
he answered me, it was a punishment suitable to their offence; for lovers, when
they fall short of their expectations, either in the pursuit or enjoyment of their
mistresses, generally say, Alas! I thought she would have loved me: I thought
she would never have pressed me to marry her: I thought she would have been a
fortune to me: I thought she would have given me all she had: I thought she
would have cost me nothing: I thought she would have asked me nothing: I
thought she would have been true to my bed: I thought she would have been
dutiful and modest: I thought she would never have kept her gallant. So that
all their pain and damnation arises from—I thought this, or that, or so.

In the middle of them was Cupid, a little beggarly rogue, and as naked as
he was born, only here and there covered with an old kind of embroidery; but
whether it was the workmanship of Disease or Industry, I could not perfectly
discover; and near him was this inscription:

> *Many a good fortune goes to wrack,*
> *And so does many an able back:*
> *With following whores, and cards, and dice,*
> *We're pox'd and beggar'd in a trice.*

I suppose, said I, by these rhymes that the poets must not be far off; and
the word was hardly out of my mouth when I discovered prodigious numbers
of them through a park-pale. I stopped to look upon them, for it seems in hell
they are not called Poets now, but Fools. One of them showed me the women's
quarter there hard by, and asked me what I thought of it, and of the handsome
ladies in it. Is it not true, says he, that a buxom lass is a kind of half chambermaid to a man? When she has stripped him, and brought him to bed, she has
done her business, and never troubles herself any farther about the helping
him up again, and dressing him. How now, said I, have ye your quirks and
conceits in hell? In troth ye are pleasant, but I thought your edge had been taken
off. With that, out came the most miserable wretch of the whole company, laden
with irons: Ah! cried he, how heartily do I wish that the first inventor of
rhymes and poetry were here in my place; and then he thus poetically made
his moan:

Oh, this damned trade of versifying,
Has brought us all to hell for lying?
For writing what we do not think,
Merely to make our verses chink;
For, rather than abuse the metre,
Black shall be white, and Paul be Peter.
One time I call'd a lady whore,
For which I'm only damn'd the more:
Yet not from malice, Jove's my witness,
But merely for my verse's fitness.
Now we're all made, said I, if luck hold,
And then I call'd a fellow cuckold;
At last I circumcis'd, 'tis true,
A Christian, and baptis'd a Jew.
Nay, I've made Herod innocent,
For rhyming too long parliament:
Now, to conclude, we're all undone,
For jingling rhyme or awkward pun:
And for a little jingling pleasure,
Condemn'd to torments without measure:
Which is a little hard in my sense,
To fry thus for poetic license.
'Tis not for sin of thoughts or deed,
But for bare sounds and words, we bleed;
While the cur Cerberus lies growling,
In concert with our caterwauling.

There cannot be a more ridiculous piece of madness, said I, than yours, to be poetizing in hell. The humour sticks close sure, or the fire would have fetched it out else. Nay, said a devil, these versifiers are a strange generation of buffoons: the time that others spend in tears and groans for their sins and follies, these wretches employ in songs and madrigals; and, if they chance to light upon the critical minute, and get a snap at a lady, all is worth nothing, unless the whole kingdom ring of it, in some miserable copy of verses or other, under the name forsooth of Phillis, Chloris, Silvia, or the like: and the goodly idol must be decked and dressed up with diamond, pearl, rubies, musk, and amber: and both the Indies are too little to furnish eyes, lips, and teeth, for this imaginary goddess:

yet, after all this magnificence and bounty, it would put the poor devil's credit upon the stretch, to take up an old petticoat in Long-lane, or a pair of cast-off shoes at the next cobbler's. Besides, we can give no account either of their country or religion. They have Christian names, but most heretical souls; they are Arabians in their hearts, and in their language Gentiles; but, to say the truth, they fall short of right Pagans in their manners. If I stay here a little longer, said I to myself, this spiteful devil will tap me over the knuckles ere I am aware; for I was half jealous that he imagined me already a piece of a poet.

To avoid being discovered, I retired; and my next visit was to the impertinent devotees, whose very prayers are made up of impiety and extravagance. Oh! what sighing was there, what sobbing, what groaning and whining. Their tongues were tied up to a perpetual silence, their souls drooping, and their ears condemned to hear eternally the frightful cries and reproaches of a wheesing devil, greeting them after this manner: O ye impudent and profane abusers of prayer and holy duties, that treat the Lord of heaven and earth in his own house with less respect than you would do a merchant upon 'Change, sneaking into a corner with your execrable petitions, for fear of being overheard by your neighbours; and yet, without any scruple at all, ye can expose and offer them up to that Eternal Purity! Shameless wretches that ye are! "Lord (says one) take the old man my father to thyself, I beseech thee, that I may have his office and estate. Oh that this uncle of mine would march off! There is a fat bishopric and a good deanery; the devil may take the incumbent so I had the dignity. Now for a lusty pot of guineas, or a lucky hand at dice, if it be thy pleasure, and then I would not doubt of good matches for my children. Lord make me his majesty's favourite, and thy servant, that I may get what is convenient, and keep what I have gotten. Grant me this, and I do hereby engage myself to entertain six blue-coats, and bind them out to good trades; to set up a lecture for every day of the week; to give one third part of my clear gains to charitable uses, and another towards the repairing churches, besides paying all honest debts, so far as may stand with my private convenience." Blind and ridiculous madness! for dust and ashes thus to reason and condition with the Almighty! for beggars to talk of giving, and obtrude their vain and unprofitable offerings upon the inexhaustible fountain of riches and bounty! To pray for those things as blessings which are commonly showered down upon us for our confusion and punishment. And then, in case your wishes take effect, what becomes of all the sacred vows and promises ye made, in storms, sickness, or adversity? So soon as ye have gained your port, recovered your health, or patched up a broken fortune, you show yourselves a pack of cheats; your vows and promises are not worth so many rushes; they are forgotten with your dreams; and to keep a promise upon devotion that you made out of necessity, is by no means an article of religion. Why do you not ask for peace of conscience, increase of grace, the aid of the blessed Spirit? But you are too much taken up with the things of this world to attend those spiritual advantages and treasures, and to consider that the most acceptable sacrifices and oblations you can make to the Almighty, are purity of mind, an humble spirit, and a fervent charity. The Almighty is pleased with being often called upon, that he may often pour down his blessings upon his petitioners: but such is the corruption of human nature, that men seldom think of him, unless under affliction, and therefore it is that they are so often visited; for by adversity they are brought to the knowledge and exercise of their duty. I would now have you consider how little reason there is in your ordinary demands: Put the case that you have your asking, what are you the better for the grant, since it fails you at last, because you do not ask aright? When you die, your estate goes to your children, and, for their parts, you are scarce cold before you are forgotten. You are not to expect they should bestow much upon works of charity; for, if nothing went that way while you were living, they will live after your example when you are dead; and, besides, there is no merit in the case. At this word, some of the poor creatures were about to reply, but the devils had put barnacles upon their lips, that hindered them.

From thence I went to the witches and wizards, such as pretend to cure man and beast by charm, words, amulets, characters; and these were all burning alive. These, says a devil, are a company of deceitful rogues, the most accursed villains in nature. If they help one man, they kill another, and only remove the disease from a worse to a better: and yet there is no clamour against them neither; for, if the patient recover, he is very well satisfied, and the doctor gets both reputation and reward for his pains; if he dies, his mouth is stopped, and forty to one but the next heir does him a good turn for the dispatch: So that, hit or miss, all is well at last. If you enter into a debate with them about their remedies, they will tell you they learnt the mystery of a certain Jew, and there is the original of the secret. Now to hear these quacks give you the history of their cures, is beyond all the plays and farces in the universe. You shall have a fellow tell you of fifteen people who were run clean through the body, and for three days carried their puddings in their hands, but in four-and-twenty-hours he made them quite whole again, and not so much as a scar was left for a remembrance of the orifice. Ask him when and where? You will find it some twelve hundred leagues off, in *terra incognita*, at that time when he was physician in ordinary to a great prince that died above five-and-twenty years ago.

Come, come, cried a devil, make an end of this visit, and you shall see those now that Judas told you were ten times worse than himself. I went along with him; and he brought me to a passage into a great hall, where there was a filthy smell of brimstone, and a company of match-makers, as I thought at first; but they proved afterwards to be alchemists; and the devils examining them upon interrogatories, were filthily put to it to understand their gibberish. Their talk was much of planetary metals: gold they called Sol; silver, Luna; tin, Jupiter; and copper, Venus. They had about them their furnaces, crucibles, coals, bellows, clay, minerals, dung, man's blood, powders and alimbecks. Some were calcining, others washing; here purifying, there separating, fixing what was volatile in one place; and rarifying what was fixed, in another: some were upon the work of transmutation, and fixing of Mercury, with monstrous hammers, upon an anvil; and, after they had resolved the viscous matter, and sent out the subtler parts, until that they came to the coppel, all went away in fume. Some again were in hot dispute what fuel was best; and whether Raymund Lullius's fire, and no fire, could be anything else than lime; or otherwise to be understood of the light, effective of heat, and not of the effective heat of fire: others were making their entrance upon the great work, after the Hermetical method. Here they were watching the progress of their operations, and making their observations upon proportions and colour; while all the rest of these blind oracles lay waiting for the recovery of the *materia prima*, till they brought themselves to the last cast, both of their lives and fortunes; and, instead of turning base metals and materials into gold, as they pretended, made the contrary inversion, and were glad at length to take up with beggarly fools and false coiners. What a stir was there, with crying out, Look you, look you! the old father is got up again; down with him, down with him. What glossing and commenting upon the old chemical text, that says, Blessed be Heaven, that has ordered the most excellent thing in nature out of the vilest. If so, cried one, let us try if we can bring the philosopher's stone out of a common strumpet; which is, without doubt, of all creatures the vilest. And the word was no sooner out, but about two dozen whores went to pot; but the flesh was so cursedly mawkish and rotten, that they soon gave over the thought of that projection. Then they entered upon a fresh consultation, and unanimously concluded, that the mathematicians, by that rule, were the only fit matter to work upon, as being the most damnably dry, to say nothing of their divisions among and against themselves; so that, with one voice, they called for a parcel of mathematicians to the furnace, to begin the experiment. But a devil came just in the nick, and thus addressed them: Gentlemen philosophers, if you would know the most wretched and most contemptible thing in the world, it is an alchemist; and we are of opinion that you will make as good philosopher's stones as the mathematicians: however, for curiosity's sake, we will try for once; and so he threw them all together into a huge cauldron, where, to say the truth, the poor wretches suffered contentedly, out of a desire, I suppose, to help on toward the perfecting of their operation.

On the other side were a knot of astrologers, and one among the rest that had studied necromancy or palmistry, who took all the damned by the hands, one after another. One he told that it was as plain as the nose on his face that he was to go to the devil; for he perceived it by the mount of Saturn. You, says he to another, have been a swinging whore-master in your days; I see that by the Mount of Venus here, and by her girdle: and, in short, he read every man's fortune in his fist. After him advanced another, creeping upon all four, with a pair of compasses betwixt his teeth, his spheres and globes about him, his Jacob's staff before him, and his eyes upon the stars, as if they were taking a height, or making an observation. When he had gazed awhile, up he suddenly starts, and wringing his hands, Good Lord, says he, what an unlucky dog was I! If I had come into the world one quarter of an hour sooner, I had been saved; for just then Saturn shifted, and Mars was lodged in the House of Life. One that followed him bade his tormentors be sure he was dead; for, says he, I am a little doubtful of myself, in regard that I had Jupiter for my ascendant, and Venus in the House of Life, and no malevolent aspect to cross me; so that, according to the rules of astrology, I was to live exactly one hundred and one years, two months, six days, four hours, and three minutes. The next that came up was a geomancer; one that reduced all his skill to certain little points, and by them would tell you, as well things past as to come. These points he bestowed at a venture among several unequal lines; some long, others short, like the fingers of a man's hand; and then, with a certain rabble of mysterious words, he proceeded to his calculation, upon even or odd, and challenged the whole world to allow him the most learned and infallible of the trade.

He was followed by several great masters of the science, as Haly, Gerrard, Bartholomew of Parma, and one Goudin, a familiar friend and companion of the great Cornelius Agrippa, the famous conjurer; who, though he had but one soul, was set burning in four bodies: I mean the four damnable books he left behind him. There was Trithemius, too, with his Polygraphy and Stenography;

that had now devils enough, though in his life-time his complaint was that he could never sufficiently have their company. Over against him was Cardan; but they could not set their horses together, because of an old quarrel concerning which was the more impudent of the two. And there I saw Mizaldus tearing his beard, in rage, to find himself pumped dry; and that he could not fool on to the end of the chapter. Theophrastus was there too, bewailing himself for the time he had spent at the alchemists bellows. There was also the unknown author of Glavicula Solomonis, and the Hundred Knights of Spirits; with the composer of the book, *Adversus Omnia Pericula Mundi.* Taisnerus, too, with his book of Physiognomy and Chiromancy; and he was doubly punished; first for the fool he was, and then for those he had made. Though, to give the man his due, he knew himself to be a cheat; and that he who gives a judgment upon the lines of a face, takes but a very uncertain aim. There were magicians, necromancers, sorcerers and enchanters innumerable; besides several private boxes that were kept for lords and ladies, and other personages of great quality, that put their trust in these disciples of the devil, and go to fortune-tellers for resolution in cases of death, love, or marriage; and now and then to recover a gold watch, or a pearl necklace.

At no great distance from these were a company of handsome women, that were tormented in the quality of witches, which grieved my very heart to see it. But to comfort me, What, says a devil, have you so soon forgot the roguery of these carrions? Have you not had trial enough yet of them? They are the very poison of life, and the only dangerous magicians that corrupt all your senses, and disturb the faculties of your soul; these are they that cozen your eyes with false appearances, and set up your wills in opposition to your understanding and reason. It is right, said I, and now you mind me of it; I do very well remember that I have found them so; but let us proceed, and see the rest.

I was scarce gone three steps farther when I was got into such a dark dismal place, that it was a mercy we knew where we were. There was, first, at the entrance, Divine Justice, most dreadful to behold; and a little beyond stood Vice, with a countenance of the highest pride and insolence imaginable. There was Ingratitude, Malice, Ignorance, incorrigible Infidelity, brutish and head-strong Disobedience, rash and imperious Blasphemy, with garments dipped in blood, eyes sparkling, and a hundred lungs barking at Providence and vomiting rage and poison. I went in, I confess, with fear and trembling; and there I beheld all the sects of idolaters and heretics that ever yet appeared upon the stage of the universe; and at their feet, in glorious array, was lascivious Barbara, second wife to the Emperor Sigismond, and the queen of harlots: one that agreed with Messalina in this, that virginity was both a burden and a folly; and that in her whole life she was never either wearied or satisfied: but herein she went beyond her, in that she held the mortality as well of the soul as of the body; but she was now better instructed, and burnt like a bundle of matches.

Passing forward still, I saw a fellow in a corner all alone, with the flame about his ears, gnashing his teeth and blaspheming through fury and despair. I asked him what he was, and he told me he was Mahomet. Why then, said I, thou art the most accursed reprobate in hell, and hast brought more wretches hither than half the world beside; and Lucifer has done well to allot thee a quarter here by thyself, for certainly thou hast well deserved the first place in his dominions. But, since every man chooses to talk of what he loves, I pray thee, good imposter, tell me what is the reason that thou hast forbidden wine to all thy disciples? Oh, says he, I have made them so drunk with my Alcoran, they need no other intoxication. But why hast thou forbidden them swine's flesh, too? said I. Because, says he, I would not affront the ham; for water upon gammon would be false heraldry. And beside, I never loved my people well enough to afford them the pleasure either of the grape or the spare-rib: nay, and for fear they should chance to grope out the way to Heaven, I have established my power and my dominion by force of arms, without subjecting my laws to idle disputes and discourses of reason. Indeed, there is little reason in my precepts, and I would have as little in their obedience. I have a vast number of disciples; but I think they follow me more out of appetites than religion, or the miracles I work. I allow them liberty of conscience; they have as many women as they please, and do what they please, provided they meddle not with government. But look about you now, and you will find that there are more knaves than Mahomet.

I did so, and found myself presently in the midst of a ring of heretics, and their adherents, many of which were ready to tear the throats of their leaders. One, among the rest, was beset with a brace of devils; and either of them had a pair of bellows, puffing into each ear fire instead of air, which made him a little hot-headed. There was another, that, as I was told, was a kind of Simoniac, and had taken up his seat in a pestilential chair; but it was so dark, that I could not discern whether it was a Pope or a Presbyter.

By this time I had enough of hell, and began to wish myself out again; but, as I was looking about for a retreat, I stumbled upon a long gallery before I was aware; and there I beheld Lucifer himself, with all his nobility about him,

H

male and female; for let married men say what they will, there are she devils
too. I should have been very much at a loss what to do, or how to behave myself
among so many strange faces, if one of the ushers had not come to me and told
me that, being a stranger, it was his majesty's pleasure I should enter, and have
free liberty of seeing what was there to be seen. We exchanged a few compli-
ments; and then I began to look about me; but never did I see a palace so
furnished, nor indeed comparable to it.

Our furniture, at the best, is but a choice collection of dead and dumb
statues or paintings, without life, sense, or motion; but there all the pieces were
animated, and no trash in the whole inventory. There was hardly anything to
be seen but emperors and princes, with some few, perhaps, of their choicest
nobility. The first seat was taken up by the Ottoman family; and after them
sat the Roman emperors in their order and the Roman kings down to Tarquin
the Proud; besides highnesses and graces, lords spiritual and temporal, innumerable. My lungs now began to call for a little fresh air; and I desired my guide to
show me the way out again. Yes, yes, with all my heart, says he; follow me. So
saying, he carried me away by a back passage into Lucifer's house-of-office,
where there was I know not how many tun of sir-reverence, and bales of flattering panegyrics, not to be numbered; all of them licensed and entered according
to order. I could not but smile at this provision of tail-timber; and my guide took
notice of it; who was a good kind of a damned devil: but still I teased him
to be gone; till at length he led me to a little hole, like the vent of a vault; and
I crept through it as nimbly as if the devil himself had given me a lift at the
crupper; when, to my great astonishment, I found myself in the park again,
where I begun my story: but not without an odd medley of passions, partly
reflecting upon what others endured; and in part, upon my own condition of
ease and happiness, that had deserved, perhaps, the contrary, as well as they.
This thought put me upon a resolution of leading such a course of life for the
future, as I might not come to feel these torments in reality, which I had now
only beheld in vision. And I must here entreat the reader to follow my example,
without making any farther experiment; and likewise not to cast an ill construc-
tion upon a fair meaning. My design is to discredit and discountenance the works
of darkness, without scandalizing of persons; and I am certain this discourse will
never be reckoned a satire, as it treats of none but the damned.

VII

OF HELL REFORMED

So great was the uproar in hell not long since, that the oldest of all the devils never knew the like. The inhabitants expected nothing less than an absolute dissolution of their empire: the devils fell upon the damned, and the damned fell upon the devils, without knowing one from the other; and all running to and fro like mad: in short, it was no other than a general rebellion. This hurly-burly lasted a good while, before any mortal could imagine the meaning of it: at length, there came certain intelligence of a monstrous talker, a pragmatical meddling undertaker, and an old gouvernante, that had knocked off their shackles, and made all this havoc; by which the reader may know what kind of cattle these are, who can make hell itself more dangerous and unquiet.

During all this noise, Lucifer went howling up and down, and bawling for chains, handcuffs, bolts, manacles, shackles, and fetters, to secure his prisoners again; when, in the middle of his career, he and the babbler or undertaker I told you of, met each other; and after a little staring at one another in the face, the babbler first began: Prince of mine, says he, you have a pack of lazy, droning devils in your dominions that look after nothing, but sit with their arms and legs across and suffer all your affairs to go to ruin. You have many abroad too, upon commission, that have stayed out their time, and yet can give you no account of what they have been doing. The gouvernante, who had been blowing the coals and whispering sedition from one to another, chanced to pass by while he was thus speaking; and stopping short, thus addressed herself to Lucifer: Look to yourself, cried she, there is a desperate plot upon your diabolical crown and dignity. There are two tyrants in it, three parasites, a world of physicians, and a whole legion of lawyers and attorneys. One word more in your

115

ear : there is among them a mongrel priest, a kind of lay-elder, that will go near to sit upon your skirts, if you have not a care of him.

The Prince of devils, when he heard her mention priest and lay-elder, looked as pale as death, and stood still as mute as a fish, while his very looks discovered his apprehensions. After a little pause, he roused himself as out of a trance : A priest, do you say, a lay-elder, tyrants, lawyers, physicians—A composition to poison all the devils in hell, and purge their very guts out! with that, away he went to visit the avenues and set his guards; when who should he meet next but the meddler in a monstrous hurry : nay then, says he, here is the forerunner of ill-luck. But what is the matter? The matter! cried the meddler : and then, with a deal of tedious and impertinent circumstances he told him that several of the damned had contrived to escape, and that there was a design to call in four or five regiments of hypocrites and usurers, under a pretence of establishing a better intelligence betwixt earth and hell. He had not yet been done, if Lucifer would have found ears; but he had other work to do, for neck and all was now at stake; and so he went about his business; putting all in a posture of defence, and strengthening his guards. For the farther security of his royal person, he ordered into his own immediate regiment several reformadoes of the society, whom he very well knew would not forsake him.

He began his survey in the vaults and dungeons, among his gaolers and prisoners. The babbler marched in the van, breathing an air that kindled and inflamed whatever he passed without giving any light; and setting people together by the ears, who knew not for what reasons. In the second place, the gouvernante, as full of news and tattle as she could hold, and telling her tale all all the way she went. In the rear of her, followed the meddler, leering as he passed along, first on one side, then on the other, without ever moving his head; and making his addresses to every soul he saw in his way. He gave one a bow, the other a kiss; Your most humble servant to a third; and, Can I serve you, Sir? to a fourth; but every compliment was worse to the poor creatures than the fire itself. Ah, traitor! says one; for pity's sake away with this tormentor! cries another. This fellow is hell upon hell, says a third.—As he trudged on, there was a rabble of rascals got together, and in the middle of the crowd, a most eminent knight of the post; a great master of his trade, who was reading a lecture to that venerable assembly of the noble mystery of swearing and lying; and would have taught any man, in one quarter of an hour, to prove anything upon oath that he never saw nor heard of in his life. The doctor no sooner saw the meddler than up he started in a flight. How now, says he, is that devil here I came hither on purpose to avoid him; and, if I could but have dreamed he would have been in hell, I would undoubtedly have gone to paradise.

At this instant, we heard a great and confused noise of arms, blows and outcries; and presently we discovered several persons falling bloodily one upon another; and, in short, with such fury that neither tongue nor pen can describe the battle. One of them appeared to be an emperor; for he was crowned with laurel, and surrounded with a grave sort of people, who looked like counsellors or senators, and had all the old statutes and records at their fingers ends. By these they endeavoured to make out, That a king might be killed in his personal capacity, and his politic capacity never be the worse for it : and upon this point, they were at daggers drawn with the emperor. Lucifer then came roundly up to him; and, with a voice that made hell tremble, What are you, Sir, says he, who take upon you thus in my kingdom? I am the great Julius Caesar, said he, who, in this general tumult, thought to have revenged myself upon Brutus and Cassius, for murdering me in the senate, under colour, it would seem, of affecting the common liberty; whereas the traitors did it merely out of envy, avarice and ambition. It was the emperor, not the empire, they hated. They pretended to destroy me for introducing a monarchy; but did they overthrow the monarchy itself? No, on the contrary, they confirmed it; and did more mischief in killing me than I did in dissolving their republic : however, I died an emperor; these villains carried only the infamy and brand of regicides to their graves; and the world has ever since adored my memory, and detested theirs.— Tell me, said he, ye cursed blood-hounds, turning towards them, whether was your government better, think ye, in the hands of your senators, a company of talking gown-men who knew not how to keep it, or in the hands of the soldier who won it by his merit? It is not the drawing of a charge, or the making of a fine oration, that fits people for government; nor will a crown fit well upon the head of a pedant; but let him wear it who is worthy of it. He is the true patriot who advances the glory of his country by actions of bravery and honour. Which has more right to rule, think ye; he that only knows the laws, or he that maintains them? The one only studies the government, the other protects it. Wretched republic! Thou callest it freedom to obey a divided multitude, and slavery to serve a single person; and when a company of covetous little fellows are got together, they must be styled Fathers of their country, forsooth; and shall one generous person take up with the name of Tyrant? Oh, how much better had it been for Rome to have preserved that one son who made her mistress of the world, than the multitude of fathers, who, by so many intestine wars, rendered her but a step-mother to her own children! How barbarous and cruel are ye, so much as to mention the name of a commonwealth! consider, that, since the people tasted of monarchy, they have preferred even the worst of princes, as Nero, Tiberius, Caligula, and Heliogabalus, before your tribe of senators.

Brutus was very much confounded at this discourse of Cæsar; but at length, with a feeble and trembling voice, he thus spoke: Gentlemen of the senate, do you not hear Cæsar? Or will you add sin to sin, and suffer all the blame to be cast upon the instruments, when you yourselves were the contrivers of the villainy; why do ye not answer? Cæsar speaks to you as well as us. Cassius and myself were but your bravos, and governed by your persuasions and advice, little dreaming of that insatiable ambition which lay lurking under the gravity of your long beards and robes: but it is the practice of you all to arraign that tyranny in the prince which you would exercise yourselves; in effect, when you have gotten power, and the colour of authority in your hands, it is more danger-ous for a prince not to comply with you than for a vassal to rebel against his prince.—To what end served your perfidious and ungrateful treason? make answer to Cæsar. But for our part, in the conscience of our sin, we feel the severity of our punishment.

No sooner had he said this, than up started a hollow-eyed supercilious senator, who had been of the conspiracy, and was then blazing like a pitch-barrel, and with a feeble voice asked Cæsar, what reason he had to complain? for, Sir, says he, if King Ptolemy murdered Pompey the Great, upon whose score he held his kingdom, why might not the senate as well kill you, to recover what you have taken from them? And, in the case betwixt Caesar and Pompey, let the devils themselves be judges. As for Achilles, who was one of the murderers, what he did was by Ptolemy's command; and then he was but a free-booter neither, a fellow that had got his living by rapine and plunder: but Caesar was undoubtedly the more infamous of the two. It is true, he wept at the sight of Pompey's head, but such tears did he shed as were more treacherous than the steel which killed him. And how cruel that compassion and revengeful that pity, which made thee a more barbarous enemy to Pompey dead than living? Oh! that ever two hypocrite eyes should creep into the first head of the world! In a word, the death of Caesar has been the recovery of our republic, if the multi-tude had not called in others of his race to the government, which rendered thy fall the very Hydra of the empire.

We had had another skirmish upon these words, if Lucifer had not ordered Cæsar to his cell again, upon pain of death; and there to abide such correction

as belonged to him, for slighting the warnings he had of his disaster: Brutus
and Cassius were turned over to the politic fools: and the senators were dis-
patched away to Minos and Rhadamanthus, and there to sit as assistants on the
Devil's bench.

  After this I heard a murmuring noise as of people talking at a distance;
and, by degrees, I made it out, that they were wrangling and disputing still
louder and louder, till at length it was but a word and a blow; and the nearer
I came, the greater was the clamour. This made me mend my pace; but before
I could reach them, they were altogether by the ears in a bloody fray: they
were all of them persons of great quality; emperors, magistrates and generals of
armies. Lucifer, to end the quarrel, commanded peace and silence, which they
all obeyed; but it vexed them very much to be taken off in the full career of their
fury and revenge. The first that spoke was a fellow so marred with wounds and
scars that I took him at first for an indigent officer, but he proved to be Clitus,
as he said himself: but one at his elbow told him he was saucy, for presuming
to speak before his time; and so desired audience of Lucifer, for the high and
mighty Alexander, the son of Jupiter, and the emperor and terror of the world.
He was going on with his qualities and titles: but an officer cried, Silence, and
bade Clitus begin, which he took very kindly, and thus said:

  May it please your majesty, I was the first favourite of this prince; who
was then lord of the known world, who bore the title of the king of kings, and
boasted himself to be the son of Jupiter Ammon; yet after all this glory and
conquest, he was himself a slave to his passions; he was rash and cruel, and
consequently incapable either of counsel or friendship. In my life-time, I was
near him, and served him faithfully; but it seems, he did not entertain me so
much for my fidelity, as to augment the number of his flatterers: I, however,
found myself too honest for a base office; and still, as he ran into any foul
excesses, I took the freedom, with all possible modesty, to show him his mistakes.
One day, as he was talking slightly of his father Philip, that valiant prince, from
whom he received both his honour and his being, I told him frankly what I
thought of that ingratitude and vanity; and desired him to treat his dead father
more reverently, as a prince worthy of eternal honour and respect. This com-
mendation of Philip so enraged him that he immediately seized a partisan and
struck me dead on the spot with his own hand. After this I asked where was his
divinity, when he gave Abdolominus, a poor garden-weeder, the kingdom of
Sidonia? which was not, as the world would have it, out of any consideration
of his virtue, but to mortify and take down the pride and insolence of the Per-

sians. Meeting him here just now in hell, I asked him what was become of his father Jupiter, that he so much boasted of? and whether he was not yet convinced that all flatterers were a parcel of villains? who, with their incense and altars, would persuade him that he was of divine extraction and heir-apparent to the throne and thunder of Jupiter? This, even now, was the ground of our quarrel. But, invectives apart, who but a tyrant would have put a loyal subject to death, only for his affection and regard to the memory of his departed sire? How barbarously did he treat his favourites, Parmenio, Philotas, Calisthenes and Amintas? so that, good or bad, it is crime enough to be the favourite of a tyrant; as, in the course of human life, every man dies, because he is mortal; and the disease is rather the pretext of his death, than the cause of it. You will find now, says the Prince of devils, that tyrants will show their people many a dog-trick when the humour takes them. The good they hate, for not being wicked; and the bad, because they are no worse. How many favourites have you ever seen come to a fair and timely end? Remember the emblem of the sponge; for that is the use which princes make of their favourites; they let them suck and fill, and then squeeze them for their own profit.

Just as he said this, there was heard a lamentable cry; and at the same time, a venerable old man, as pale as if he had no blood in his veins, came up to Lucifer, and told him that his emblem of the sponge came very pat to his case; for, says he, I was a great favourite, and a great hoarder of treasure: a Spaniard by birth; the tutor and confident of Nero; and am called Seneca. Indeed his bounties were to excess: he gave me without asking; and in taking, I was never covetous but obedient. It is in the nature of princes, and it befits their quality, to be liberal where they take a liking, both of honour and fortune: and it is hard for a subject to refuse without some reflection upon the generosity or discretion of his matter; for it is not the merit or modesty of the vassal, but the glory of the prince, that is the question; and he is the best subject who contributes the most to the splendour and reputation of his sovereign. Nero, indeed, gave me as much as such a prince could bestow; and I managed his liberalities with all the moderation imaginable; yet all was too little to preserve me from the strokes of envious and malicious tongues, which would have it that my philosophizing upon the contempt of the world was nothing else but a mere imposture, that thereby, with less danger and notice, I might feed and entertain my avarice, and with fewer competitors. Finding my credit with my master declining, it became me to provide some way or other for my quiet, and to withdraw myself from being the mark of a public enemy; so I went directly to Nero, and, with all possible respect and humility, made him a present of all those bounties he had bestowed upon me. The truth is, I had so great a passion for his service, that neither the severity of his nature, nor the debauchery of his manners, could ever deter me from exhorting him to noble courses, and paying him all the duties of a loyal subject. Especially in cases of cruelty and blood, I laid it always home to his conscience, but all in vain; for he put his mother to death, laid the city of Rome in ashes, and, indeed, depopulated the empire of honest men. These horrid and impolitical severities drew on Piso's conspiracy, which was better laid than executed: for, upon the discovery, the prime instruments lost their lives; and, by Divine Providence, this prince was preserved, in order, as one would have imagined, to his repentance and change of life: but, upon the issue, the conspiracy was prevented, and Nero never the better. At the same time, he put Lucan to death, only for being a better poet than himself; and, if he gave me my choice what death to die, it was rather cruelty than pity; for, in the very deliberation on which death to choose, I suffered all, even in the terror and apprehension that made me refuse the rest. The choice I made was, to bleed to death in a bath; and I finished my own dispatches hither; where, to my farther affliction, I have again encountered this imfamous prince, studying new cruelties, and instructing the very devils themselves in the art of tormenting.

Upon this, Nero advanced, with his ill-favoured face and shrill voice. It is very well, says he, for a prince's favourite, or tutor, to be wiser than his master; but let him manage that advantage with respect; and not, like a rash and insolent fool, make proclamation presently to the world, that he is the wiser of the two. While Seneca kept himself within these bounds, I was his sincerest friend; and the love I had for that man was the glory of my government; but when he came to publish once, what he should have dissembled and concealed, that it was not Nero, but Seneca, that ruled the empire, nothing less than his blood could make satisfaction for so intolerable a scandal; and from that hour I resolved his ruin. I had rather suffer what I do a hundred times over, than entertain a favourite who should raise his credit upon my dishonour. Whether I have reason on my side or no, I appeal to all this princely assembly. Draw near, I beseech you, as many as are here; and speak freely, my royal brethren: did you ever suffer any favourite to escape unpunished, that had the insolence to write, I and my king; to make a stalking horse of majesty; and who published himself a better statesman than his master? No, no, they all cried out; it never was, and never shall be endured, while the world lasts; for we have left our successors under an oath to look particularly to this. It is true, a wise counsellor at a prince's elbow is a treasure, and ought to be esteemed, while he makes it his business to cry up the abilities and justice of his monarch; but, in the instant that his vanity transports him to the contrary, away with him, and down with him, for there is no enduring it.

All this, cried Sejanus, does not yet concern me; for, though I had indeed more brains than Tiberius, yet I so ordered it, that he had the credit in public of all my private advices; and so sensible he was of my service, that he made me his partner and companion in the empire: he caused my statues to be erected, and invested them with sacred privileges. Let Sejanus live, was the daily cry of the people; and, in truth, my well-being was the joy of the empire; and far and near there were public prayers and vows offered up for my health. But what was the end of all? When I thought myself surest in my master's arms and favour, he let me fall; nay, he threw me down, caused me to be cut in pieces; delivering me up to the fury of a cruel and enraged multitude, that dragged me along the streets; and happy was he that could get a piece of my flesh to carry upon a javelin's point in triumph. And it had been well, if this inhuman cruelty had stopped here: but it extended to my poor children; who, though unconcerned in my crimes, were yet to partake in my fate. A daughter I had, whom the very law exempted from the stroke of justice, because of her virginity; but, to clear that scruple, she was condemned first to be ravished by the executioner, and then to be beheaded, and treated as her father. My first failing was upon temerity and pride: I would outrun my destiny, defy fortune, and, as to Divine Providence, I looked upon that as a ridiculous thing. When I was once out of the way, I thought doing worse was somewhat in order to being better; and then I began to fortify myself by violence, against craft and malice. Some were put to death, others banished; and, in short, both celestial and terrestrial powers have declared themselves against me. I had recourse to all sorts of ill people, and bad means. I had my physician for poisoning, my assassins for revenge; I had my false witnesses, and corrupt judges; and, in truth, what instrument of wickedness had I not? and all this, not upon choice or inclination, but purely out of the necessity of my condition. Whenever I should come to fall, I was certain of being forsaken, both by good and bad; and therefore I shunned the better sort, as those that would only serve to accuse me; but the lewd and vicious I frequented, to increase the number of my accomplices and make my party the stronger. But, after all, if Tiberius was a tyrant, I will swear he was never so by my advice: on the contrary, I have suffered more from him for plain dealing, and dissuading him, than the very subjects of his severity have commonly suffered by him. I know, it is charged upon

me, that I stirred him up to cruelty, to render him odious, and to ingratiate
myself with the people. But who was his adviser, I pray, in this butcherly proceeding against me? Oh Lucifer, Lucifer! you know very well that it is the
practice of tyrants, when they do amiss themselves and set their people
a-grumbling, to lay all the blame, and punishment, too, upon the instrument,
and hang up the minister for the master's fault. This is the end of all favourites,
cries one. Not a halfpenny matter, if they were all served so, says another. Every
historian, continued Sejanus, has his saying upon this catastrophe; and sets up
a buoy, to warn after ages of the rock of court-favours. The greatness of a
favourite, I must own, proclaims the greatness of his maker; and the prince who
maintains what he has once raised, does but justify the prudence of his own
choice: if ever he undoes what he has done, he publishes himself to be light
and inconstant, and thereby does as bad as to declare himself, even against himself, of the enemy's party.

Plantian advanced next, Severus's favourite; he that was thrown out of
a garret-window to divert the people. My condition in the world, says he, was
perfectly like that of a rocket or firework. I was carried up to a prodigious height
in a moment, and all the people's eyes were upon me, as a star of the first
magnitude; but my glory was very short-lived and down I fell into obscurity
and ashes. After him appeared several other favourites, and all of them hearken-
ing to Belisarius, the favourite of Justinian; who, blind as he was, had already
knocked twice with his staff and, shaking his head, with a weak and complaining
voice, desired audience, which was at length granted him. Silence being commanded, he thus spoke:

Princes, before they destroy the creatures they have raised and chosen,
should do well to consider that cruelty and inconstancy is a much greater infamy
to the prince, than any effects of it can be to the favourite. For my own part,
I served an emperor, who was both a Christian and a great lover and promoter
of justice; but yet, after all the services I had done in several battles and adventures, insomuch that he was actually become my debtor to the very glory of his
empire, my reward, in the end, was to have my eyes put out and, with a dog
and bell, to be turned out to beg from door to door: thus was that Belisarius
treated, whose very name formerly was worth an army, and who was the soul
of his friends, as well as the terror of his enemies. But a prince's favour is like
quicksilver, restless and slippery, never to be fixed, nor even secured. Force it,
and it spends itself in fumes; sublime it, and it is a mortal poison; handle it only,
and it works itself into the very bones; in short, all that have to do with it, live

pale, and die trembling. At these words, the whole band of favourites set up a hideous and heavy groan, trembling like aspen-leaves; and, at the same time, reciting several passages out of the prophet Habakkuk, against careless and wicked governors, by which threatening is given to understand that the Almighty, when he thinks proper to destroy a wicked ruler, does not always punish one potentate by another, and bring his ends about by a trial of arms, or the event of a battle, but many times makes use of things the most abject and vile, to confound the vanity and arrogance of the mighty; and makes even worms, flies, caterpillars and lice to serve him as the ministers of his terrible justice; nay, the stone in the wall, and the beam in the house, shall rise in judgment against them.

This discourse might have gone farther, but that the company presently parted to know the meaning of a sudden noise they heard, which half deafened the auditory; but what was it at last but a scuffle between the gownmen and brothers of the blade. There were persons of great honour and learning, young and old, engaged in the fray. The men of war were at it, clashing with their swords; and the gentlemen of the long robe fencing; some with tostatus, others with huge pandects, that with their old wainscot covers were as good as bucklers, and would now and then give the foe a heavy rebuke over the head. The combat had certainly been very bloody, if one of Lucifer's constables had not commanded them, in the king's name, to keep the peace, which made it a drawn battle. With that, one of the combatants, with the best face he had, said aloud, If you knew, gentlemen, either us, or our quarrel, you would say we had reason and perhaps side with us. At that instant there appeared Dormitian, Commodus, Caracalla, Phalaris, Heliogabalus, Alcetes, Andronicus, Bulsiris and Oliver Cromwell, with several great personages more; which, when Lucifer saw, he disposed himself to treat their majestical appearance as much to their satisfaction as was possible. Whereupon a grave and venerable man appeared, with a great train at his heels, who were all bloody and full of the marks they had received under these tyrants' persecution.

You have here before you, cried the old man, Solon; and these are the seven sages, natives of Greece, but celebrated throughout the world. He there in the mortar, is that Anaxarchus who was pounded to death by the command of Nicroceon. He with the flat nose is Socrates. This little crump-shouldered wretch was the famous Aristotle; and that other there, the divine Plato. Those in the corner, are all of the same profession too; grave and learned philosophers, who have displeased tyrants with their writings: in short the world is stored with their works and hell with the authors. To come to the point, most mighty Lucifer, we are all of us dealers in politics, great writers, and deep read men in the maxims of state and government. We have digested policy into a method, and laid down certain rules, by which princes may make themselves great and beloved. We have advised them impartially to administer justice, to reward virtue, both military and civil, to employ able men, banish flatterers, to put men of wisdom and integrity in places of trust, to reward or punish without passion, and according to the merits of the cause, as God's viceregents. But this is our offence: we name nobody, we design nobody; but it is crime enough to wish well to the encouragers of virtue. After this, turn towards the tyrants: Oh, cruel princes, said he, these glorious kings and emperors, from whom we took the model of our laws and instructions, are now in state of rest and comfort, while you are tormented. Numa is now a star in the firmament, and Tarquin a firebrand in hell. The memory of Augustus and Trajan is still fresh and fragrant, when the names of Nero and Sardanapalus are more putrid and nauseous than their carcases.

As soon as Dionysius the tyrant heard this, with his companions about him, he could not contain himself, but cried out in rage, That rogue of a philosopher has told a thousand lies. Legislators! Yes, yes, they are sweet legislators and princes have many a fair obligation to them. No, no, sirah, said he to Solon, you are all of you a company of quacks; you prate and speculate things you know nothing about; and with your devilish moralities set the people agog upon liberty; cry up the doctrine of free-born subjects; and then our portion is persecution in one world, and infamy in the other.

We shall have a fine time of it, my most gracious prince, cried Julian the apostate, staring Lucifer in the face, when these dunghill-pedants, a company of cock-brained, ridiculous, mortified, ill-bred, beggarly ragamuffins, shall come to erect a committee for politics, and pass sentence upon governors and governments, styling themselves, forsooth, the supporters of both, without any more skill than my horse in what belongs to either. Tell me, says he, if an illustrious prince had not better be damned than subject himself to hear one of these rascals, with a bald head, and his eyes crept into his sockets, pronouncing for an aphorism, that a prince who looks only to one, is a tyrant, and that a true king is the shepherd and servant of his people. Ah, rash and besotted coxcombs! If a king looks only to others, who shall look to him? As if princes had not enemies enough abroad, without being so to themselves, too, but you may write your hearts out, and never amend us. Where is our sovereignty, if we have not our subjects' lives and estates at our mercy? And where is our absolute power, if we submit to the counsels of our vassals? If we have not enough to satisfy our appetites of avarice and revenge, we want power to discharge the noblest ends of government. These contemplative idiots would have us make a choice of good officers to keep the bad in order; which were a madness in our condition. Let them be complaisant, and no matter for any other merit or virtue. A parcel of good offices, well disposed among a pack of cheats and atheists, will make us a party another day; whereas all is lost that is bestowed upon honest men; for they are our enemies. Speak truth then, all of you, and shame the devil; for the butcher fats his sheep only for the shambles.

I need say no more, I suppose, to stop your mouths; but here is an orator who will read you another lecture on politics, perhaps a better than any you have yet had, if you will but attend. Photinus, advance, said Julian, and speak your mind. Whereupon a brazen-faced fellow came forward, with a hanging look, and twenty other marks of a desperate villain; who, with a hellish yell and three or four wry mouths for a prologue, thus began:

The cruel advice of one of PTOLEMY'S *courtiers, about the killing of* POMPEY; *from Lucan's* PHARSALIA, *Book VIII.*

Great and mighty Ptolemy, methinks, under favour, that we are now slipped into a debate a little beside the business. The question is, whether Pompey shall be delivered up to Cæsar or no; that is to say whether, in reason of state, it ought to be done; and we are formalizing the matter, whether in point of equity and justice it may be done. Bodies politic have no souls; and never did any great prince turn a council of state into a court of conscience, but he repented it. Kingdoms are to be governed by politicians, not by casuists; and there is nothing more repugnant to the true interest of crowns and empires, than in public cases to make a scruple of private duties. The argument is this: Pompey is in distress, and Ptolemy under an obligation; so that it were a violation of faith and hospitality not to relieve him. Now, give me leave to reason in the other way. Pompey is forsaken, and persecuted by the gods; Cæsar upon the heels of him, with victory and success. Shall Ptolemy now ruin himself to protect a fugitive, against both Heaven and Cæsar? I must own, where honesty and profit are both of a side, it is well; but, where they disagree, the prince who does not quit his religion for his convenience, falls into a direct conspiracy against himself: he shall lose the hearts of his soldiery, and the reputation of his power. Whereas, on the contrary, the most odious tyrant in the world shall be able to keep his head above water, if he will but give a general licence to commit every species of wickedness. You will say this is impious; but I say, what if it be, who shall call you to account? These deliberations are only for subjects which are under a command, and not for sovereign princes, whose will is a law.

> *He's not form'd for a court*
> *Who is too devout.*

To conclude, since either Pompey or Ptolemy must suffer, I am absolutely for the saving of Ptolemy, and the presenting of Pompey's head, without any more ado, to Cæsar. A dead dog can do no harm.

As soon as Photinus had finished, Domitian appeared in a rage; and, hauling in poor Suetonius after him, like a bear to the stake. There is not in nature, says he, so cursed a generation of scribbling rogues as these historians : we can neither be quiet for them living nor dead; for they haunt us in our very graves; and, when they have vented the humour and caprice of their own brains, the infamous production, forsooth, must be called *The Life of such an Emperor*. As an instance of their villainy, I will show you what this impertinent chronicler says of me : He squandered away his treasure, says he, in expensive building, plays, and presents to the soldiers.

Now would I know which way it could have been better employed.

In another place, he says, Domitian had some thought of easing himself in his military charges, by reducing the number; but that he durst not do, for fear some of his neighbours should put an affront upon him : so that, to make himself whole, he fell to raking and scraping whatever he could get either from the dead or the living; and any rascal's testimony was proof enough for a confiscation; for there needed no more to ruin an honest man, than to tell a tale at court, that such a one had spoken ill of the prince.

Is this the way of treating majesty? What could this impudent pedant have said worse, if he had been speaking of a pick-pocket or a pirate? But they make no difference between princes and thieves.

He says farther, Domitian made seizure of several estates, without the least right to them, and there went no more to his title, than for a false witness to depose, that he heard the defunct declare, before he died, that he made Cæsar his heir. He set up such a tax upon the Jews, that many of them denied their religion to avoid it : and I remember that, when I was a young fellow, I saw an old man of fourscore-and-ten taken up on suspicion by one of Domitian's spies, and turned up in a public assembly, to see if he was circumcised.

Be you now judges, gentlemen, if this be not a most intolerable indignity?

Can I be answerable for the actions of my inferior officers? I am surprised that my successors should ever suffer these scandalous reports to be published, especially against a prince who had laid out so much money in repairing the libraries that were burnt.

It is true, said Suetonius, in a melancholy tone; and I have not forgotten to make mention of it to your honour: but what will you say if I show you, in a warrant under your hand, this execrable and impious blasphemy? "It is the command of your Lord and God." And, in fine, if I am to speak nothing but truth, where is the cause of your complaint? I have written the lives too of the great Julius Cæsar and the divine Augustus; and the world will not say I have executed them very well: but for yourself, and such as you, who are effectually but so many incarnate and crowned plagues, what fault have I committed in setting before your eyes those tyrannies, which heaven and earth cannot look upon but with dread and horror?

Suetonius would have said more had he not been interrupted by a babbler, who whispered Lucifer in the ear, and said, Look you, Sir, pointing with his finger, that limping devil there, who looks as if he was lamed with beating the hoof, has been abroad in the world these twenty years, and is just now returned. Come hither, sirrah, cries Lucifer. Whereupon the poor cur went wriggling up towards his prince. You are a fine rogue to be sent off an errand, are you not, says Lucifer, to stay twenty years out, and come back again even as wise as you went? What fools have you brought now, or what news from the other world? Your Highness, replied the devil, has too much honour and justice to condemn me unheard: wherefore be pleased to remember that, at my going out, you gave me charge of a certain merchant; it cost me the first ten years of my time to make him a thief and ten more to keep him from turning honest again and restoring what he had stolen. A fine fetch for a devil this, is it not? cried Lucifer: but hell is no more like the hell it was when I knew it first, than chalk is like cheese: and the devils, now-a-days, are so damnably insipid and dry, they are hardly worth the roasting. A senseless puppy! to come back to me with a story of Waltham's calf, that came nine miles to suck a bull: but he is yet but a novice in his business. Upon which Lucifer bade one of his officers take him away, and put him to school again; for I perceive he is a rascal, says he; and he has even been rogueing at a play-house, when he should have been at church.

Just after this, several men came running as hard as they could drive from behind a little hill, after a company of women: the men crying out, Stop, stop; and the women crying for help. Lucifer commanded them all to be seized, and asked the meaning of their running. Alas, alas! cried one of the men, quite out of breath, these carrions have made us fathers, though we never had children. Govern your tongue, sirrah, cried a devil of honour, out of respect to the ladies, and speak truth, for it is quite impossible you should be fathers without children. Pardon me, said the fellow, we were married men, and honest men, and good house-keepers, have borne offices in the parish, and have children that call us father; but it is a strange thing that, after we have been abroad, some of us for seven years together, others as long bed-rid, and so impotent, that we have been reckoned among the dead, and yet our wives have brought us every year a child, whom we were such fools as to keep and bring up, and give ourselves to the devil at last to get them estates, out of a charitable persuasion, forsooth, that they might yet be our own; though, for a twelvemonth together, perhaps, we never so much as examined whether our wives were fish or flesh: but now, since the mothers are dead, and the children grown up, we have found out the tools who made them. One has the coachman's nose, another the gentleman-usher's legs, a third a cousin-German's eyes; and some, we are to presume, conceived purely by strength of imagination, or else by the ears, like weasels.

Upon this there appeared a little remnant of a man, a dapper Spaniard, with a besom-beard and a voice not unlike the yelping of a cur. As he came near the company, he let up his throat, and called out, Ah, Jade! I shall now take you to task, you whore you, for making me father my negro's bastards, and for the estate I settled upon him. I ever misdoubted foul play, but should never have dreamed of that ugly toad, when there was such a choice of handsome young fellows about us; but I suppose you had them too. Frequently have I cursed the monks to the pit of hell, Heaven forgive me for it; for the strumpet would be constantly gadding abroad, under pretence of going to confession, though, to tell the truth, I was never any great friend to penance and mortification. But then would I be continually disclosing my mind to this cursed Moor. I cannot imagine, said I, where this mistress of thine should commit all the sins that she goes out every hour of the day to confess at yonder monastery? Upon which the villain would answer me, Alas, good lady! I would even venture my soul for her's with all my heart; she spends all her time, you see, in holy duties. I was at that time so innocent, that I suspected nothing more than a pure respect and civility to my wife; but I have learned better since; and that effectually his soul and her's were commonly ventured in the same bottom; yes, and their bodies, too, as I perceived by their piebald issue; for the bastards take after both father and mother. So that, at this rate, cried the adopted fathers, the husband of a

I

whore has a pleasant time on it. First, he is subjected to all the pukings, longings, and peevish importunities that a breeding woman gives those about her, till she is delivered; and then comes the squalling of the child, and the tittle-tattle gossiping of the child, and the tittle-tattled gossipings of the nurse and midwife, who must be well treated too, well lodged, and well paid into the bargain. A sweet baby, says one to the jade who is the mother of it, it is even as like the father as if he had spit it out of his mouth: it has the very lips, the very eyes of him; when it is no more like him than an apple is like an oyster: and, at last, when we have borne all this, and twenty times more, in the other world, with a Christian patience, we are hurried away to hell, where we lie like a company of damned cuckolds of us; or, for aught I see, in *Sæcula seculorum;* which is very hard and, in truth, out of all reason.

I cut this visit short, to see what news in a deep vault near at hand, where we heard a great bustle and contest betwixt several souls and the devils. There were the presumptuous, the revengeful, and the envious, gaping and crying out as if they would break their hearts, Oh, that I could be born again! says one: Oh, that I might go back into the world again! says another: Oh, that I were but to die once more! cries a third. Insomuch that they put the devils out of all patience, with their impertinent and unprofitable witness and exclamations. Hang yourselves, cried the devils, for a pack of cheating, bawling rascals. You live again! and be born again! And what if you might do it a thousand times over? You would only die at last a thousand times greater villains than you are at present; and there would be no clearing hell of you. However, to try you, and make you know yourselves, we have commission to let you live again and return. Up then, you varlets, go, be born again; return into the world again.—Away, cried the devils, with a lusty lash at every word, and thrust hard to get them out; but the poor rogues hung back, and were struck with such a terror to hear of living again and returning to earth, that they slunk into a corner and lay as peaceably as lambs.

At length one of the company, who seemed to have somewhat more brain and resolution than his fellows, entered very gravely upon the debate, whether they should go out or not? If I should now, says he, at my second birth, go into the world a bastard, the shame would be mine, though my parents committed the fault, and I should carry the scandal and infamy of it to my grave: but suppose, however, that my mother should be honest, as that is not impossible, and I go into the world legitimate, yet how many follies, and vices, and diseases, are there that run in the blood! Who knows but I should be mad, or swear, lie, cheat or whore? nay, if I came off with a little mortification of my carcase, such as the stone, scurvy, or the pox, I were a happy man. But, oh, the lodging, the diet, and the cookery that I am to expect for a matter of nine months in my mother's belly; and then the butter and beer that must be spent to sweeten me when I change my quarters! I must come crying into the world, and be ignorant of what it is to live till I die, and then as ignorant of death too till it is past. I fancy my swaddling-clothes and blankets to be worse than my winding-sheet; my cradle represents my tomb; and then who knows whether my nurse shall be found or no? She may overlay me, perhaps; leave me some four-and-twenty hours, it may be, without clean clouts, and a pin or two all the while perhaps up to the hilt in my backside: then follows breeding of teeth and worms, with all the gripes and disorders that are caused by unwholesome milk. These miseries are certain; and why should I endure them over again? If it happens that I pass the state of infancy without the small-pox or measles, I must then be packed away to school, to get the itch, a scald-head, or a pair of kibed heels. In winter it is ten to one but you find me with a snotty-nose; and constantly under the lash, if I either miss my lesson, or play the truant. So that, hang him, for my part, who would be born again, for anything I see yet. When I advance to manhood, the women will have me as sure as a gun; for they have a thousand gins and devices to catch woodcocks; and if ever I come to set eye upon a lass who understands dress and raillery, I am gone, if there were no lads in Christendom. But, for my part, I am as sick as a dog of powdering, curling, and playing the lady-bird. I would not for all the world be in the shoemaker's stocks, and choke myself over again in a strait cravat, only to have the ladies say, Look what a genteel shape and foot that gentleman has! And I would take as little pleasure to spend six hours of the four-and-twenty in picking gray hairs out of my head or beard, or turning white into black. To stand half ravished in the contemplation of my own shadow; to dress fine, to go to church only to see beautiful ladies; to correct the midnight air with ardent sighs and ejaculations, and to keep company with owls and bats, like a bird of ill omen; to walk the round of a mistress's lodging, and play at bo-peep, at the corner of every street; to adore her imperfections, or, as the song says—for her ugliness, and for her want of coin; to make bracelets of her locks, and truck a pearl necklace for a shoe-string. At this rate, I say, cursed again and again be he, for my part, that would live over again so miserable a life.

Being now come to write full man, if I have an estate, how many cares, suits and brangles go along with it! If I have none, what murmuring and regret at my misfortunes! By this time the sins of my youth are gotten into my bones; I grow pensive and morose; nothing pleases me; I curse old age to ten thousand devils; and the youth which I can never recover in my veins, I endeavour to fetch out of the barber's shop from perukes, razors, and patches, to conceal, or at least to disguise, all the marks and evidences of nature in her decay. Nay, when I shall never have an eye to see with, nor a tooth left in my head, gouty legs, windmills in my crown, my nose running like a tap, and gravel in my veins by the bushel; then must I make oath that all this is nothing but mere accident, gotten by lying in the field, or the like; and out-face the truth, in the very teeth of so many undeniable witnesses. There is no plague comparable to this hypocrisy of the members. To have an old sop shake his heel, when he is ready to fall to pieces and cry. These legs would make a shift yet to play with the best legs in the company; and then, with a lusty thump on his breast, fetch up a hem, and cry, Sound at my heart, boy; and a thousand other such fooleries: but all this is nothing to the misery of an old fellow in love, especially if he be put to gallant it against a company of young gamesters. Oh! the inward shame and vexation, to see himself scarce so much as neglected. It happens sometimes that a jolly lady, for want of better entertainment, may content herself with one of these reverend fornicators instead of a whetstone; but, alack! the poor man is weak, though willing; and, after a whole night spent in cold frivolous pretences and excuses, away he goes with inexpressible torments of rage and confusion about him; and many a heavy curse is sent after him, for keeping a poor lady from her natural rest to so little purpose. How often must I be put to the blush, too, when every old toad shall be calling me old acquaintance, and saying to me, Oh, Sir, it is many a day since you and I were first acquainted: I think it was in the four-and-thirtieth of the Queen that we were school-fellows: how the world is altered since! And then must my head be turned into a *mementi mori;* my flesh dissolved into rheums; my skin withered and wrinkled; with a staff in my hand, knocking the earth at every trembling step, as if I called upon my grave to receive me. Walking like a moving ghost; my life little more than a dream; my reins and bladder turned into a perfect quarry; and the urinal my whole study; my next heir watching every minute for the long-desired and happy hour of my departure; and, in the meantime, I myself become the physician's revenue and surgeon's practice: with an apothecary's shop in my guts, and every old jade calling me grandsire. No, no; I will endure no more living again, I thank you: one hell, rather than two mothers. But let us now consider the comforts of life; the humours and the manners. He that would be rich must play the thief, or the cheat; he that would rise in the world must turn parasite, informer, or projector. He that marries, ventures fair for horns either before or after. There is no valour without swearing, quarrelling, or hectoring; if ye are poor, nobody owns ye; if rich, you will know nobody; if you die young, what pity it was, they will say, that he should be cut off thus in the prime! if old, he was even past his best; there is no great miss of him: if you are religious, and frequent the church and the sacrament, you are a hypocrite; and without this, you are an atheist, or an heretic: if you are cheerful and merry, you pass presently for a buffoon; and if pensive and reserved, you are taken to be morose and censorious: courtesy is called colloguing and currying of favour; down-right honesty and plain-dealing, is interpreted to be pride and ill-manners. This is the world; and, for all that is in it, I would not have it to go over again. If any of ye, my masters, said he to his companions, be of another opinion, hold up your hands. No, no, cried they all unanimously, no more generation-work, I beseech ye; better the devils than the midwives.

The next who came was a testator, cursing and raving like a bedlamite, that he had made his last will and testament. Ah, villain! said he, for a man to murder himself, as I have done! If I had not sealed, I had not died. Of all things, next a physician, deliver me from a testament; it has killed more than the plague. Oh, miserable mortals! let the living take a warning by the dead, and make no testament. It was my great misfortune, first, to put my life into the physician's power; and then, by making my will, to sign the sentence of death upon myself, and be my own executioner. Put your soul and your estate in order, says the doctor, for there is no hope of life; and the word was no sooner out, but I was so wise and devout, forsooth, as to fall immediately upon the prologue of my will, with an, in the name of God, Amen. When I came to dispose of my goods and chattels, I pronounced these bloody words (I would I had been tongue-tied when I did it); I make and appoint my son my sole executor. *Item*, To my dear wife I give and bequeath all my plays and romances, and all the furniture in the rooms upon the second storey. To my very good friend, T.B., my large tankard, for a remembrance. To my foot-boy, Robin, five pounds, to bind him an apprentice. To Betty, who waited upon me in my sickness, my little caudle-cup. To the doctor, my fair table-diamond, for his care of me in my illness. After signing and sealing, the ink was scarcely dry upon the paper, but methought the earth opened, as if it had been hungry, to devour me. My son and my legatees were presently casting it up how many hours I might have yet hold it out. If I called for the cordial juleep, or a little of Dr. Gilbert's water, my son was taking possession of my estate; my wife so busy about the beds and hangings that she could not attend it; the boy and the wench could understand nothing but about their legacies; my very good friend's mind was wholly upon his tankard; my kind doctor, I must confess, took occasion, now and then, to handle my pulse and see whether the diamond were of the right black-water or no: if I asked him what I might eat, his answer was, Anything, anything; even what you like best yourself: at every groan I fetched they were calling for their legacies, which they could not have till I was dead. But if I were to begin the world again, I think I should make another kind of testament: I would say, A curse upon him that shall have my estate when I am dead; and may the first bit of bread he eats from it, choke him. The devil take what I cannot carry away; and him, too, who struggles for it, if he can catch him. If I die, let my boy Robin have the strappado three hours a day, to be duly paid him during my life. Let my wife die of the mother; but let her first live long enough to plague the damned doctor, and indict him for poisoning her poor husband. To speak sincerely, I can never forgive that dog-leech. Was it not enough to make me sick when I was well, without making me dead when I was sick ? And not to rest there neither, but to persecute me in my grave, too? But, to say the truth, this is only neighbour's fare; for all those fools who trust in them, are served in the same manner. A vomit or a purge is as good a passport into the other world as a man can deire; and then, when our heads are laid the scandal they cast upon our bodies and memories is insupportable. Heaven rest his soul, cries one, he killed himself with a debauch. How is it possible, says another, to cure a man who eats everything that comes in his way? He was a madman, cries a third, a mere sot, and would not be governed by a physician. His body was as rotten as a pear: he had as many diseases as a horse; nor was it in the power of man to save him: and, truly, it was well that his hour was come, for he had better a great deal die well than live on as he did. Thieves and murderers that ye are! You yourselves are that hour you talk of. The physician is only death in a disguise, and brings his patient's hour along with him. Cruel people! is it not enough to take away a man's life, and, like common hangmen, to be paid for it when you have done; but you must blast the honour too of those you have despatched, to excuse your ignorance? Let but the living follow my counsel, and write their testaments after this copy; they shall then live long and happy, and not go out of the world, at last, like a rat, or be cut off in the flower of their days, by these counterfeit doctors of the faculty of their closestool.

The poor man plied his discourse with so much gravity and earnestness, that Lucifer began to imagine what he said was true : but because all truths are not to be spoken, especially among the devils, where hardly any are admired; and for fear of mischief, if the doctors should come to hear what had been said, Lucifer immediately ordered the fellow to be gagged, and put in security for his good behaviour.

No sooner was his mouth stopped, than another was opened; and one of the damned came running across the company, and so up and down, backward and forward, like a cur that had lost his master, bawling as if he had been deprived of his senses, and crying out, Oh! where am I? where am I? I am abused? I am choused : what is the meaning of all this? Here are damning devils, tempting devils, and tormenting devils; but the devil a devil can I find of the devils that brought me hither; they have gotten away my devils : where are they; give me my devils again.

No wonder that the company stared, to see a fellow hunting for devils in hell, where they are to be found in crowds in every corner : but as he was in his hurry, a gouvernante caught him by the arm, and gave him a half turn, and stopped him. Old Lucky Bird, says, she, if thou wanted devils here, where dost thou expect to find them? He knew her as soon as he saw her. And art thou here, old Beezelbub in Petticoats? said he; the very picture of Lucifer, the coupler of male and female, the buckler and thong of letchery; the multiplier of sin, and the guide of sinners; the interpreters betwixt whores and knaves; the preface to the remedy of love, and the prologue to the critical minute : speak, and without more ado, tell me where are the devils and their dams that brought me hither? These are none of them. No, no, I am not such a fool as to be trepanned and spirited away by devils with tails, horns, bristles and wings, that smell as if they had been smoked in a chimney corner. The devils that I look for, are worse than these. Where are the mothers that play the bawds to their own daughters? and the aunts that do as much for their nieces, and make them caper and sparkle like wildfire? the black eyed girls that carry fire in their eyes, and strike as sure as a lance from the hand of a cavalier? Where are the flatterers that speak nothing but pleasing things? the incendiaries, that are the very canker of human society? Where are the story-mongers? the masters of the faculty of lying; that report more than they hear, affirm more than they know, and swear more than they believe? those slanderous backbiters, that, like vultures, prey only upon carrion? Where are the hypocrites, that turn devotion into interest, and make a revenue of a commandment; that pretend ecstacy when they are drunk, and utter the fumes and dreams of their luxury for revelations; that make chapels of their parlours, preachments of their ordinary entertainments; and everything they do is a miracle; who divine all that is told them, and raise people to life again, that counterfeit sick when they should work; and give an honest man to the devil with a Deo Gratias? These are the devils I would be at; these are they that have damned me; look them out and find them for me, you impudent hag, or I shall be so bold as to search your French hood for them. Thus saying, he fell upon the poor gouvernante, tore off her head-dress, and laid about him so furiously, that there would have been no getting him off, if Lucifer had not made use of his absolute authority to quiet him.

As soon as the fray was composed, we heard the shutting of bars and bolts, the opening of doors and hinges that creaked for want of grease, and a strange humming of a vast crowd of people. The first that appeared were a company of bold, talkative and painted old women; but jolly and gamesome, tickling and toying with one another, as if they had never seen thirteen; and carrying it out with an air of much satisfaction and content. The babbler was somewhat scandalized at their behaviour, and told them how ill they did to be merry in hell; and several others admired as much, and asked them the reason of it, considering their condition. Upon this, one of the gang that was very thin and pale, and raised upon a pair of heels that made her legs longer than her body, respectfully told Lucifer that, at their first coming, they were as sad as it was possible for a company of damned old jades to be; but, says she, we were a little comforted when we heard of no other punishment here than weeping and gnashing of teeth, and in some hope to come off upon reasonable terms; for we have not among us so much as a drop of moisture in our bodies, nor a tooth in our heads. Search then presently, cried the intermeddler, squeeze the balls of their eyes, and let their gums be examined, you will find snags, stumps or roots, or enough of somewhat or other there to spoil the jest. Upon the scrutiny, they were found so dry, that they were good for nothing in the world, but to serve for tinder or matches; and so they were disposed of in the devil's tinder boxes.

While they were casing up the old women, there came on several people of various sorts and qualities, that called out to the first they saw. Pray you, gentlemen, said they, before we go any farther, will you direct us to the Court of Rewards? How is that, cried one of the company, I was afraid we had been in hell; but since you talk of rewards, I hope it is but purgatory. Good, good, said the whole multitude, you will quickly find where you are. Purgatory! cried the meddler; you have left that up the hill there, upon the right hand: this is hell, and a place of punishment; here is no registry of rewards. Then we are mistaken, said he that spoke first. How so? cried the meddler. You shall hear, said the other. We were in the other world entitled to the order of the Squires of the Pad, and borrowed now and then a small sum upon the king's highway; we understood somewhat too of the cross-bite, and the use of the frail dye. Some of our conscientious and charitable friends would fain have drawn us off from the course we were in, and to give them their due, bestowed a great deal of good counsel upon us, to very little purpose, for we were in a pretty way of thriving, and had gotten a habit, and could not leave it. We asked them, what would you have us do; money we have none, and without it there is no living: should we stay till it were brought, or come alone, how would you have a poor wretched being to live, that has neither estate, office, master, nor friend to maintain him; and is quite out of his element, unless he be either in a tavern, a bawdy-house, or a gaming-ordinary? Now that is the man that Providence has appointed to live by his wits. Our advisers saw there was no good to be done, and went away, telling us, that in the other world we should meet with our reward.

They would tell us sometimes how base a thing it was to defame the house, and abuse the bed of a friend. Our answer was ready: Well! and had we not better do it there, where the house is open to us, the master and lady kind, the occasion fair and easy; than to run a caterwauling into a family, where every servant in the house is a spy, and perhaps, a fellow behind every door in the house, with a dagger or pistol in his hand to entertain us? Upon this, our grave counsellors, finding us so resolute, even gave us over; and told us, as before, that in the other world we should meet with our reward. Now, taking this to be the other world these honest men told us of, we are inquiring after our rewards.

Abominable scoundrels! said an officer of justice there at hand; how many of your reprobate companions have squandered away their fortunes upon whores and dice, exposing not only their wives and children, but many a noble family to a shameful and irreparable ruin? And let any man put in a word of wholesome advice, their answer is, Tush, tush, our wives and children are in the hand of Providence, and let him provide for the rooks that feed the ravens. Then it was told you, you shall find your reward in the other world, and the time is now come wherein you shall receive it. Up, up then, you cursed spirits, and away with them. At which word, a legion of devils fell upon the miserable caitiffs, with whips and firebrands, and gave them their long expected reward; and at every lash, a voice was heard to say, In the other world you shall receive your reward. These wretches, in the meanwhile, damning and sinking themselves to the pit of hell, still, as if they had been upon earth, and vomiting their customary and execrable blasphemies.

Just as this storm blew over, there approached a prodigious number of bailiffs, sergeant, catchpoles, and other officers of prey, with the devil that was to tempt thieves upon earth, bound hand and foot, and a foul accusation against him. Whereupon Lucifer, with a fell countenance, took his seat in a flaming chair, and called his officers about him. So soon as the prince had taken his place, a certain officer began his report : Here is before thee, cried he, a devil, most mighty Lucifer, that stands charged with ignorance in his trade, and the shame of his quality and profession; instead of damning men, he has made it his business to save them. The word *save* put the court in such a rage, that they bit their lips till the blood startled, and the fire sparkled at their eyes; and Lucifer, turning about to his attorney, Who would ever have thought, said he, that so treacherous a villain could have been harboured in my dominions? It is most certain, my gracious lord, replied the attorney, that this devil has been very diligent in drawing people into thefts and pilferies; and then, when they came to be discovered, they are clapped up and hanged, or some mischief or other : but still, before execution, the ordinary calls them to penance, and frequently the toy takes them in the head, to confess and repent; and so they are saved. Now this silly devil thinks, that when he has brought them to steal, murder, coin and the like, he has done his part, and so he leaves them; whereas he should stick close to them in prison, and tempt them to despair and make away with themselves : but when they are once left to the priest, he commonly brings them to a sight of their sins, and they escape. Now this simple devil was not aware, it seems that many a soul goes to heaven from the gallows, the wheel, and the faggot; and this failing has lost your Highness many a fair purchase. Here is enough, cried the president, and their needs no more charge against him. The poor devil thought it was high time to speak now, when they were just upon the point of passing his sentence; and so he cried out : My lord, I beseech you hear me : for though they say the devil is deaf, it is not meant of your Greatness. Upon a general silence, he thus spoke :

I cannot deny, my lord, but Tyburn is the way to Paradise, and many a man goes to heaven from the gallows : but if you will set those that are damned for condemning others, against those that are saved from the gallows, hell will be found no loser by me at the foot of the account. How many marshal's men, turnkeys and keepers have I sent you, for letting a coiner make his escape now and then with his false money, always provided they leave better money instead of it? How many false witnesses, and knights of the post, that would set their consciences like clocks, to go faster or slower, according as they had more or less weight; and swear *extempore* at all rates and all prices? How many solicitors, attorneys and clerks, that would draw you up a declaration or an indictment so slily, that I myself could hardly discover any error in it; and yet, when it came to the test, it was as plain as the nose on a man's face; that is to say again, provided they were well paid for the fashion? How many jailors that would wink at an escape for a paltry bribe? and how many attorneys that would give you despatch or delay in proportion as they were greased? Now, after all this, what does it signify, if one thief of a thousand comes to the gallows; he only suffers because he was poor, and that there may be better trading for the rich; and without any design in the world to suppress stealing. Nay, it frequently happens, that they who bring the malefactor to the gibbet are the worse criminals of the two: that they are never looked after; or, if they should be, they have tricks enough to bring themselves off: so that it fares in this case, as it did with him that had his house troubled with rats, and would needs take in some cats to kill them; the rats would be nibbling at his cheese, his bacon, a crust of bread, and now and then a candle's end; but when the cats came, down went a milk-bowl, and away goes a brace or two of partridges, or a couple of pigeons; and the poor man must be content to go supperless to bed. In conclusion, the rats were troublesome, the cats were intolerable. And then there is this in it: suppose one poor fellow hangs and goes to heaven, I do but give him in exchange for two hundred at least, that deserve to be hanged, but escape and go to hell at last. Besides, a thief upon a gibbet is as good as a roasted dog in a pigeon-house; for you shall immediately have two or three thousand witches about him for snips of his halter, an eye, tooth, or a collop of fat; which is of great use in many of their charms. But, in fine, let me do what I will, my services are not understood. My successor, perhaps, will discharge his duty better: and, indeed, I am very well content to resign my commission; for, to say the truth, I am in years and would gladly have a little rest now in my old age; which I rather propose to myself in the service of some other than where I am.

Lucifer heard him very patiently and gave him all the satisfaction imaginable; strictly charging the evil spirits that had abused him to do so no more, upon hazard of pains corporal and spiritual. They desired him too, that he would not resign his employment; for he was strong enough yet to do very good service in it: but to think of easing himself by going to a pretender, he would find himself mistaken; for it was a duty he would never be able to endure. Well! says he, even what your Highness pleases. But, truly, I thought a devil might have lived very comfortably in that condition : for he has no more to do, that I can see, than to keep his ears open, and learn his trade. For, put the case it should be some pretender to a good office, or a fat bishopric; though the fathers and councils are against pretenders in this case, I fancy to myself all the pleasures that may be. It is as good as going to school; for these people teach the devils their ABC; and all we have to do is to sit still and learn.

After him came the demon of tobacco, which, I must own, greatly astonished me. I have, indeed, often said to myself, certainly these smokers are possessed; but I could never swear it till now. I have, said the devil, by bringing this weed into Spain, revenged the Indians upon the Spaniards for all the massacres and butcheries they committed there; and done them more mischief than ever Colon, Cortez, Almero or Pizarro did in the Indies. By how much is it more honourable to die upon a sword's point, by gun-shot, or at the mouth of a cannon, than for a man to snivel and sneeze himself into the other world? or to go away again in a megrim, or a spotted fever, perchance? which is the ordinary effect of this poisonous weed. It is with tobacconists as it is with demoniacs under exorcism; they fume and vapour, but the devil sticks to them still. Many there are that make a very idol of it; they admire, they adore it; tempting and persecuting the people to take it; and the bare mention of it puts them into an ecstasy. In the smoke, it is a probation for hell, where another day they must endure smoking; taken in powder at the nose, it draws upon youth the incommodity of old age, in the perpetual annoyance of rheum and drivel.

Then came the devil of subornation, which was a good complexioned and well-timbered devil, to my great amazement, I must acknowledge; for I had never seen any devils till now but what were very ugly; the air of his face was so familiar to me, that, methought, I had seen it in a thousand several places; sometimes under a veil, sometimes uncovered; now under one shape, and then under another. One while he called himself Child's play; another while, Kind Entertainment; here, Payment; there, Restitution; and in a third place, Alms : but, to tell the truth, I could never learn his right name. I remember in some places I have heard him called Inheritance, Profit, Patrimony, Gratitude. Here he was called Doctor; there, Bachelor : with the lawyers, solicitors, and attorneys, he passed under the name of Right; and the confessors called him Charity.

He was well accompanied, and styled himself Lucifer's lieutenant; but there was a devil of consequence that powerfully opposed him, and made this proclamation of himself : Be it known, says he, that I am the great embroiler,

and politic entangler of affairs: the deluder of princes, the pretext of the unworthy, and the excuse of tyrants. I can make black white; and give what colour
I please to the foulest actions in nature. If I had a mind to overturn the world,
and put all in general confusion, I could do it; for I have it in my power, to
banish order and reason out of it; to turn importunity into merit, example into
necessity: to give law to success, authority to infamy, and credit to insolence.
I have the tongues of all counsellors at my girdle; and they shall speak neither
more nor less than just as I think proper. In short, that is easy to me which others
account impossible; and while I live, you need fear neither virtue nor justice, or
good government in the world. This devil of subornation that talks of his
lieutenancy, what could he ever have done without my aid? he is a rascal that
no person of quality would admit into company, if I did not fit him with vizors
and disguises. Let him be silent, then, and know himself; and let me hear no
more of these disputes about the lieutenancy of hell; for I have Lucifer's broad
seal to show my title to it.

For my part, exclaimed another rebellious spirit, I am none of those humble-
minded devils that can content myself to hold the door upon occasion, or knock
under the table, and play at small game, rather than stand out; but few words
among friends are best; and when I have spoken three or four, let him come
up that chooses. I am then, says he, the devil-interpreter, and my business is to
gloss upon the text; in which case the cuckolds are very much beholden to me;
for I have much to say for the honour of the calling. How should a poor fellow,
that has a handsome wench to his wife, and never a penny to live on, hold up his
head in the world, if it were not for that quality? I have a pretty faculty in doing
good offices for distressed ladies at a time of need; and I make the whole sex
sensible how great a folly and madness it is to neglect those sweet opportunities.
Among other secrets, I have found out a way to establish an office for thievery,
where the officers shall be thieves, and justify it when they have done. Here they
stopped.

A few moments after, there appeared another devil, of about a foot and a
half high. I am, says he, a devil of small size, and perhaps one of the least in hell;
and yet the door opens to me as well as to another, for I never come empty-
handed. Why, what have you brought then? says the meddler, and came up to
him. What have I brought? replied he; I have brought a perfect magpie, and a
cynical flatterer; they are two pieces that were in high esteem in the cabinet of
two mighty princes; and I have brought them for a present to Lucifer. With
that Lucifer cast his eyes upon them, and with a haughty grin, You do well, says

he, to say you had them at court; and I think you should do well to carry them thither again; for I had rather have their room than their company.

Then came another dwarf-devil, complaining that he had been about six years concerned with so infamous a rascal, that there was no good to be done with him; for the bad, as well as the better sort, were scandalized at his conversation. A mighty piece of business! cried the gouvernante; and could you not have gotten him a handsome post or employment? that would have made him good for something, and you might have done his business.

In the meantime, the babbler went whispering up and down, and finding faults; till at length he came to a huge heap of sleeping devils in a corner that were faggoted up, and all mouldy and full of cobwebs; these he immediately gave notice of, and they cut the band to give them air. With much ado they waked them, and asked, What devils they were? What they did there? and why they were not upon duty? They fell a yawning, and said that they were the devils of luxury. But they said that since the women had taken a fancy to prefer money to their modesty and honour, there had been no need of a devil in the case to tempt them: it is but showing them the merry skinners, continued they, and they will dart like larks, and fall down before you; and then you may even do what you will with them, and take them up in a purse-net. Gold supplies all imperfections, it makes an angel of a crocodile, turns a fool into a philosopher, and a dressing-box, well lined, is worth twenty thousand devils: so that there is no temptation like a present: and take them from top to bottom, the whole race of women is frail: and one thread of pearl will do more with them than a million of fine stories.

Just as this devil gave over speaking, we heard another snorting; and it was well we did so, for we had trod upon his belly else. He was laid hold of upon suspicion that he slept a dog-sleep, or rather the sleep of a contented cuckold, that would spoil no sport where he made none. I am, says he, the nun's devil; and, for want of other employment, I have been three days asleep here as you found me. My mistresses are now choosing an abbess, and always when they are at work I make holiday, for they are all devils themselves then; there is such canvassing, flattering, importuning, cajoling, making of parties; and in a word so general a confusion that a devil among them would do more hurt than good Nay the ambitious make it a point of honour, upon such an occasion, to show how they can outwit the devil: and if hell should be found in danger of a peace, it is my advice that you presently call in a convention of nuns to the election of an abbess; which would most certainly reduce it to its ancient state of sedition, mutiny and confusion, and bring us all, in effect, to such a pass that we should not easily know one another.

Lucifer was very well pleased with the advice, and ordered it to be entered upon the register, as a sure expedient to suppress any disorders that might happen for the future, to the disturbance of his government. After which he commanded the issuing of a summons, to all his company and liverymen, who immediately appeared in vast crowds; while, with a hideous yell, he thus addressed them:

THE
DECREE OF LUCIFER

TO our well beloved and despairing legions and esteemed subjects, lying under the condemnation of perpetual darkness, that lived pensioners to Sin and Death for their pay-master, greeting.

I have assembled you together to inform you that there are two devils who pretend a claim to the honour of our lieutenancy; but we have absolutely refused to gratify either the one or the other in that point, out of a singular affection and respect of our right trusty and esteemed cousin, a certain she devil, who is more worthy of it than any other.

As soon as they heard this, they fell to whispering and muttering, and staring one upon another; till at last Lucifer, observing it, told them never to trouble themselves to guess who it might be; but bring Good Fortune, alias Madam Prosperity to him; who presently appeared in the tail of the assembly, and, with a proud and haughty air, marched up, and planted herself before the degraded seraphim, who looked her kindly in the face, and then continued his speech.

It is our will, pleasure, and command that, next and immediately under our proper person, you pay all honour and respect to the Lady Prosperity, and obey her as the most mighty and supreme governess of these our realms. These titles and qualities we have conferred upon her as due to her merit; for she hath damned more souls than you all together. She it is that makes men cast off all dread of their heavenly Father, and love of their neighbour. She it is that makes men place their sovereign good in riches: that engages and entangles men's minds in vanity; strikes them blind in their pleasures; loads them with treasure, and buries them in sin. Where is the tragedy that she has not played her part in? Where is the stability and wisdom that she has not staggered? Where is the folly that she has not improved and augmented? She takes no counsel, and fears no punishment. She it is that furnishes matter for scandal, experience for story;

that entertains the cruelty of tyrants, and bathes the executioners in innocent blood. How many souls that lived innocent while they were poor have fallen into impiety and reprobation as soon as ever they came to drink of the enchanted cup of Prosperity! Go then, be as obedient to her, we charge you all, as to ourself; and know that, they that stand against Prosperity, are not for you. Let them even alone; for it is but time lost to attempt them. Take example from that impertinent devil that got leave to tempt Job; he persecuted him, beggared him, covered him all over with scabs and ulcers. Blockhead that he was! If he had understood his business he would have gone another way to work, and begged leave to have multiplied riches upon him, and to have possessed him of health and pleasures—that is the trial! And how many are there that, when they thrive in the world, turn their backs upon heaven, and never so much as name their Creator but in oaths, and then, too, without thinking on him? Their discourse is all of jollities, banquets, comedies, purchases and the like; whereas, the poor man has God always in view. Lord, says he, be mindful of me, and have mercy on me, for all my trust is in thee. Wherefore, says Lucifer, redoubling his accursed clamour, let it be published forthwith throughout all our dominions, that calamities, troubles and persecutions are our mortal enemies; for so we have found them upon experience : they are the dispensations of Providence, the blessings of the Almighty, to fit sinners for himself; and they that suffer them are enrolled in the militia of heaven.

Item : For the better administration of our government, it is our will and pleasure, and we do strictly charge and command, that our devils do give constant attendance in courts of judicature; and they are hereby totally discharged from any further care of little pettifoggers, flatterers and envious persons; for they are so well acquainted with hell-road, that they will guide one another without the help of a devil to entice them.

Item : We do ordain and command, that no devil presume, for the future, to entertain any confident but Profit; for that is the harbinger that provides vice the most commodious quarter, even in the straitest consciences.

Item : We do ordain, as a matter of great importance to the conversion of our empire, that in what part soever of our realms the devil of money shall condescend to appear, all other devils there present shall rise, and, with due reverence, present him the chair, in token of their submission to his power and authority.

Item : We do expressly charge and command all our officers, as well civil as military, to employ their utmost diligence and industry for the establishing a general peace throughout the world; for that is the time for wickedness to thrive in, and every species of wickedness to flourish; as luxury, gluttony, idleness, lying, slandering, gaming and whoring; and, in a word, sin is upon the increase, and godliness in the wane; whereas, in a state of war, men are upon the exercise of valour and virtue, calling often upon Heaven in the morning, for fear of being knocked on the head before dinner; and honest men and actions are rewarded.

Item: We do, from this time forward, discharge all our officers and agents whatsoever from giving themselves any farther trouble in tempting men and women to sins of incontinence; since experience informs us, that adultery and fornication will never be left till the old woman can sin no longer. And though there be several intervals of repentance, and some faint purposes of giving whoredom over, yet the humour returns again with the next tide of blood, and concupiscence is as loyal a subject as any we have in our dominions.

Item: In consideration of the exemption aforesaid, by which means several poor devils are left without present employment; and forasmuch as there are many merchants and tradesmen in London, Paris, Madrid, Amsterdam and elsewhere, that are very charitably disposed to help people in want, especially young heirs newly at age, and spendthrifts, that come to borrow of them; but the times being dead, and little money stirring, all they can do is to furnish them with what the house affords; and if a hundred pounds or two in commodity will do them any good, it is at their service, they say. This the gallant takes up at an extravagant rate, to sell again immediately for what he can get: and the merchant has his friend to take it off under hand, at a third part of the value; which is the way of helping men in distress. Now, out of singular respect to the said merchants and tradesmen, and for their better encouragement, as also to the end that the devils aforesaid may not run into lewd courses for want of business; we will, and require, that a legion of the said devils shall always do everything in their power to aid and assist the said merchants and tradesmen in the quality of factors, to be relieved monthly by a fresh legion, or oftener, if occasion shall require.

Item: We do will and command, that all our devils, of what degree of quality soever, do henceforth entertain a strict amity and correspondence with our trusty and well-beloved the usurers, the revengeful, the envious, and all pretenders to great places and dignities: and, above all others, with the hypocrites who are the most powerful imposters in the world, and so excellently skilled in their trade, that they steal away peoples hearts and souls at the eyes and ears insensibly; and draw to themselves adoration and reward.

Item: We do further order and command that all possible care be taken for the maintaining of informers, incendiaries, and parasites, in all courts and palaces; for thence comes our harvest.

Item: That babblers, tale-bearers, incendiaries and instruments of divorces and quarrels, be no longer called fans, but bellows, as they draw and inflame, without giving any allay or refreshment.

Item: That the intermeddlers be hereafter called and reputed, The devil's body-lice, because they fetch blood of those that feed and nourish them. Lucifer then casting a sour look over his shoulder, and espying the gouvernante: I am of his opinion, cried he, that said, Let God dispose of the gouvernantes as he thinks proper; for I am in no little trouble how to dispose of them here. Whereupon the damned cried out with one voice, Oh Lucifer! let it never be said that it rained gouvernantes in thy kingdom: are we not miserable enough, without this new plague of being baited by hags? Ah, cursed Lucifer (cried everyone to himself); stow them anywhere, so they are not near me. And with that, they all clapped their tails between their legs and drew in their horns, for fear of this new torment. Lucifer, finding how the dread of the old women wrought upon his subjects, contented himself at the present to let it pass only *in terrorem;* but withal, he swore, by the honour of his imperial crown, and as he hoped to be saved, that what devil, devil's dam, or reprobate soever, should, for the future, be wanting in his duty, and in the least degree disobedient to his laws and commands, all and every the said devil, or devils, their dams, or reprobates, so offending, should be delivered to the torture of the Douegna, and tied muzzle to muzzle, so to remain for ever without relief or appeal, notwithstanding any law, statute or usage to the contrary. But in the interim, he cried, Cast them into that dry ditch, that they may be ready for use if wanted any time else.

No sooner had the Prince of devils finished his speech, and retired to his abode, than the company, dispersing in a fright at so terrible a menace, withdrew to their different quarters: and at the same time a voice from heaven, like that of an angel, pronounced the following words: "He will never think his time ill spent in reading this discourse, who comprehends the morality of it."

THE END